Jim Patewa was born in Yengema, in the Eastern Province of Sierra Leone. He attended the United Methodist Primary School, New Site, Bo, Sierra Leone, before completing his secondary school education at the Christ The King College, Bo. Jim completed his bachelor's degree in Agriculture General at the Njala University College, Sierra Leon, in 1983. After his university education, Jim taught mathematics at the Centenary Secondary School Bo and the Sierra Leone Muslim Brotherhood Secondary School in Mile 91, north of the country.

In 1978/88, Jim worked as an agricultural officer in the Bonthe District for the National Association of Farmers of Sierra Leone. In 1988 Jim joined the Sierra Leone Church/Commission on Churches in Development (SLC/CCD), an agricultural extension rural development programme in the Pujehun District, as an agricultural extension officer/counterpart programme manager.

From 1989 to 1991, Jim served as manager, SLC/CCD programme. He was also a facilitator, for the National Development Education and Leadership Training programme (DELTA).

From 1991 to 1993, he served as a counterpart Agricultural Advisor to the development office of the Bo Anglican Diocese. In 1993, Jim completed an MSc in agricultural extension at the University of Reading, UK.

In 1996, he started a doctorate programme at the Gender Institute, London School of Economics and Political Science, on the topic: "How women can contribute to the post-war rehabilitation and development of their rural communities in Sierra Leone using the concept of social capital", which he couldn't complete owing to circumstantial constraints. In 2004, Jim completed a Diploma/MSc in social work at the University of Reading. In 2008, he completed a Diploma in Higher Practice Education in social work at the University of Reading, UK.

I dedicate this book to my wife, Jeneba Patewa, and our children, Kenneth, Janet, and Jim (Jr.), for all their support and encouragement that has led to the compilation of Indigenous Knowledge in Upland Rice Farming and Its Uses in Information Management. I also dedicate this work to my late parents, Janet Lagawo (RIP) and Alfred Kenneth Patewa (RIP), not forgetting my mother-in-law, Bintu Koroma (RIP), and my father-in-law, Kpewah Silla (RIP).

This book is dedicated, with forever loving memories, to my aunty, Wuyata (RIP), and many other aunties and uncles in my village, Kpatema (gone but not forgotten), on whose farm I had the opportunity of witnessing and appreciating what goes on in upland rice farming, not realising then that one day I will write a book on account of their art. On Aunty Wuyata's farm, I always enjoyed unrestricted liberty. It never crossed my mind to ask them questions about their farming at the time. Nonetheless, when the time was right, with the best of my insight and enquiry, I asked those questions to the farmers in the Pujehun District, to whom I wholeheartedly dedicate this book.

Jim Patewa

INDIGENOUS KNOWLEDGE ON TRADITIONAL UPLAND RICE FARMING IN SIERRA LEONE

Uses in Information Management

AUSTIN MACAULEY PUBLISHERS™

LONDON ∗ CAMBRIDGE ∗ NEW YORK ∗ SHARJAH

A CIP catalogue record for this title is available from the British Library.

ISBN 9781398444638 (Paperback)
ISBN 9781398444645 (Hardback)
ISBN 9781398444652 (ePub e-book)

www.austinmacauley.com

First Published 2023
Austin Macauley Publishers Ltd®
1 Canada Square
Canary Wharf
London
E14 5AA

I would like to acknowledge, with profound gratitude, the role of Professor Paul Richards, formerly of the London School of Oriental Studies, a veteran on the subject of indigenous knowledge, who introduced me to the concept by opening my eyes to the values of indigenous knowledge in upland rice farming. I also acknowledge the role of my friends and family, who showed interest and urged me to come this far in publishing this book.

Special acknowledgement to all those farmers whose knowledge I have captured in this book, and my former colleagues at the SLC/CCD programme, for their time and efforts, without which this book would not have materialised. And to all the readers, I dedicate this book so that it may serve not only as reading material, but also a practice manual for practical applications in the various forms that will benefit their society.

Table of Contents

Plates and Figures

Figures

Preface

This book is for farmers, students, researchers, institutions and individuals interested in promoting sustainable agriculture and environmentally friendly farming practices, irrespective of their discipline and academic background. The theme is increasing food production by using the indigenous knowledge of the local people. It helps to enhance our understanding of how we can obtain information from the knowledge on upland rice farming in Sierra Leone and manage it in increasing productivity while maintaining sustainable, environmentally friendly farming practices in the country. It is for readers who would like to read from cover to cover and others who may only want to dip into the chapters of their interest.

Upland rice farming is the major source of food production in Sierra Leone. It is arguably one of the environmentally friendly farming systems in the country in terms of low external inputs without the need for chemicals and artificial fertilizers.

Upland rice farming has survived in sustaining the livelihoods of generations past and present. Atherton (1979) cited reports that rice cultivation probably reached Sierra Leone and the West African region over several thousands of years. Despite the longevity, there could be a case for the argument that the typical traditional upland rice farming in Sierra Leone is slowly becoming a dying art. The basis for this argument could be the general trend of decline in adhering to the core principles of traditional upland rice farming practices nowadays. This could be a major contributing factor to the rapid disappearance and devaluing of indigenous knowledge in upland rice farming practices. It is only a matter of time unless there are serious efforts to rescue the knowledge base of traditional upland rice farming by collecting, documenting, formatting, archiving and transforming it for its continued usage.

I was introduced to the concept of indigenous knowledge, by Professor Paul Richards, as an undergraduate at The Njala University College, Sierra Leone, in a module on Environmental Studies in the 1982/83 academic year. He was on sabbatical leave from the School of Oriental and African Studies, University of London, United Kingdom. In that module, students worked in groups, visiting farmers in their villages and farms in the Kori Chiefdom, Moyamba District, to conduct interviews on their farming practices and related activities. I benefited from the exercise as the interpreter for my group, most of whom were overseas students. Professor Richards mentioned the fieldwork conducted by the students in his book: Indigenous Agricultural Revolution.

Inspired by the experience at The Njala University College in the 1980s, I seized the opportunity to revisit the study of farmers' indigenous knowledge seven years later while serving as manager, of the Sierra Leone Church/Commission on Churches in Development (SLC/CCD). The SLC/CCD was an agricultural and rural development project in the Pujehun District under the Anglican Diocese of Bo. The data on indigenous knowledge discussed in chapter four are from an information-gathering exercise conducted with the team of extension workers in the SLC/CCD project from 1990 to 1991. Following the interviews and information gathering, there were discussions in the villages between the farmers and the extension staff for verifications, wherein I served as a facilitator. I would mention that the information on indigenous knowledge included is only a part of what was collected. Some plant species have been omitted due to the unavailability of their botanical names.

In that participatory work, I noted that the farmers were amazed by our interest and the time we devoted to gathering the information. It showed how much we valued and appreciated their knowledge, which they had regarded as irrelevant and of no use to academics and western education. It was a remarkable demonstration of our preparedness to learn from them as change agents for us to deliver an effective and meaningful extension service. The exercise was a learning and awareness-building experience for the extension workers. It led them to discover the need to gain in-depth knowledge about the farming system that we had claimed to be the experts, professing to be the professionals with the technical knowledge and mandate to advise the farmers on their practices. I am deeply indebted in gratitude to those farmers and the team of extension workers who participated in the information gathering and the discussions that followed in the villages. Their invaluable contributions in various ways created the material that later became the manuscript.

It was only through sheer luck that the manuscript happened to be among some documents that I took with me for photocopying on a trip to Bo, on the 7 of April 1991. Little did I know, at the time, that I wasn't going to return to my base, Gobaru, in Pujehun for a long time due to rebel incursions a few days after I left. On my return, I discovered that all I left behind were lying in ruins of ashes from a fire by the rebels during their occupation. Later that year, I was offered a place for a course on Knowledge and Information Management at the University of Wageningen in the Netherlands. As a result of that offer, the manuscript became a treasured asset.

This book would not have seen daylight had I not travelled with the manuscript to the UK for a study in Agricultural Extension at the Agriculture and Rural Development Department, University of Reading, in 1993. It served as valuable learning material for a module, in that course, on Farmers' Information Management. A couple of years after my study the idea dawned on me that I should write this book.

In acknowledgement of the support I got from various individuals in bringing this book to fruition, I should start by expressing my eternal gratitude to the following people, Mr Eya David Macauley, Professor Peter Sandy and Dr Ola-Kris Akinola. I am indebted in gratitude to all three of you for your time, encouragement and advice for this book to be what it is for the intended readers. I remain forever grateful for your book reviews.

Eya is an Analyst in Geographical Information Systems & Remote Sensing (GIS/RS) in the Forensic Science Section, Integrated Services Division, Office of the Prosecutor of the International Criminal Court in The Hague, Netherlands. Eya has a speciality in geoinformation and remote sensing, which he coordinates at The Court. Eya and I have come a long way from our days at Njala University College. His knowledge of upland rice farming from participation and observations while visiting farms of relatives, like myself, puts him in a better position to see it through the lenses of his current work in GIS. Many thanks for exposing me to the usage of GIS in managing information on upland rice farming.

Peter was a Professor of Public Health at The University of South Africa in Pretoria and a Visiting Professor at Brunel University in the UK. He is a Professor Emeritus at the University of South Africa, and a Senior lecturer in Public Health at the University of West London, UK. Peter and I were schoolmates at The Christ The King College, Bo, in the 1970s, and our friendship has lasted this far. His guidance in pointing me in the right direction for relevant materials and resources has been invaluable in the final editing and trimming off the rough edges.

Ola-Kris is a senior lecturer, Playwright/Film Director and Life coach at The University of Limpopo, Republic of South Africa. Ola-Kris' comments and suggestions have been of great value to the completion of this book. I am grateful, particularly, for proofreading this book as an outsider to the farming systems in Sierra Leone.

By and large, this book is a rallying call for those with agricultural backgrounds. The choice of proof-readers from non-agricultural backgrounds was deliberate, with the objective that this book should appeal to the intended broad and varying readers from different disciplines and backgrounds. The reason is that with the increasing problems of food shortages around the world, it would appear that the goal of global food security could become attainable when agriculture and food production become everybody's business.

My thanks and gratitude go to my brother-in-law Alhaji Mustapha O Silla, for the photos of the various events and practices in upland rice farming that I have included in this book. In equal measure, I express my gratitude for the book cover capturing the beauty of a typical upland rice farm in its prime, courtesy of my brother-in-law Sadiq Silla Esq. I am very grateful.

I will like to show my gratitude to Robert Dixon, who worked in the development office of the Council of Churches, Sierra Leone, in the late 1980s and early 1990s, for giving me a copy of the first chapter of the fieldwork: "The Trees of Sierra Leone", from our discussion on the manuscript. Without the availability of The Treesd of Sierra Leone, I would not have been able to give the botanical names of the plant species. Unfortunately, the translations are unavailable in Limba, one of the main languages in the country.

My great depth of gratitude is to my wife, Jeneba, for being part of the journey from the time of the manuscript. Her patience and understanding have been the driving force behind the materialisation of this book. At times she would inevitably notice my divided attention while focusing on writing. Helpfully, she did not make it obvious or show any fuss about being ignored to avoid causing distractions. I can recall the day of her final nudge, together with my friend Tamba Sandi Ngauja, in Florida, USA, urging me that it is about time for publishing. Tamba has been a source of motivation and encouragement, for which I am sincerely grateful.

While writing this book, my son Jim developed an interest in agriculture and farming practices in Sierra Leone from reading the various chapters along the way, as I plodded on from one chapter to the next. I owe you gratitude for your feedback and encouragement. I am thankful to my daughter Janet who kept checking on me and asking how I got on during those long hours in front of the computer. I give my profound thanks and gratitude to the entire family, Jeneba, Ken, Janet and Jim, for all their support.

It is worth mentioning that many people supported me in many ways, but space does not allow me to include everyone. I do not doubt that you know how much I appreciate your support.

This book does not recommend indigenous knowledge in upland rice farming as an article of faith. Nonetheless, it is a step on the journey of discoveries that will raise questions which will need answers along the multi-faceted dimensions and pathways it has charted. It can only go this far for now with the permission of time and space.

By and large, this quote from The Letters Written by the Earl of Chesterfield to His Son encapsulates the essence of this book: "Learning (knowledge—mine) is acquired by reading books, but the much more necessary learning, the knowledge of the world, is only to be acquired by reading men and studying all the various facets of them" (Philip Stanhope, 4th Earl of Chesterfield ed. 1827). Similarly, knowledge on typical upland rice farming can be acquired by studying farmers in their various facets.

Indigenous knowledge in upland rice farming and its uses in information management is a window of learning about upland rice farmers in Sierra Leone in terms of how they manage information in their traditional farming practices. With the application of the concept of the 'Johari Window' (Luft J & Ingham H, 1955), we can see that the more we seek out the farmers to learn about their knowledge and practices, the more we make discoveries that will broaden our understanding of why they do what they do. In our interventions, we can unlock what is in their 'Blind spot', reveal the 'Unknown', and what may be 'Hidden' from the farmers, researchers and extension workers, and together we can effectively manage information in upland rice farming.

I will end the preface by thanking Austin Macauley Publishers for publishing Indigenous Knowledge on Upland Rice Farming, uses in Information Management.

Introduction

Throughout human history, people around the world have used the knowledge of their environment to sustain their lives and uphold their cultural identity. The collective body of knowledge they have gained through their intuition, experimentation, and experiential learning can be called their indigenous knowledge.

In some cultures, indigenous knowledge has continued to be based mainly on traditions, whereas, in others, as the developed western societies, it has evolved and transformed through research and scientific findings.

Traditional indigenous knowledge is experiential and is from the customs, practices, beliefs and concepts shared among the indigenous people compared with scientific knowledge, which is generally associated with the western developed countries, resulting from experimentation and universal verification.

According to published literature, the concept of indigenous knowledge received increasing importance in Africa with the emergence of ethnoscience in the development lexicon of the continent in the second half of the twentieth century. Ethnoscience relates scientific studies to the cultural practices of different races of people (Moore, Sally Falk, 1994). Studies in ethnoscience have established that indigenous knowledge systems have existed in all human societies from their origin.

With the increasing awareness of the importance of indigenous resources in sustainable agricultural development in Sierra Leone in the 1970s, the research institutions and extension services began to take a fresh look at the traditional practices and concepts in the indigenous farming systems. Shreds of evidence are in studies on upland rice farming, including those by Spencer (1974, 1975), Njoku (1979), Njoku and Karr (1973), and Richards (1985).

These studies heralded a renewed interest in the system of upland rice farming from the national research centres. The Rice Research Station in Rokupr, Northern Province, began to report encouraging results from a research programme that took local intercropping strategies as its starting point for improving upland rice yields. A high-yielding upland rice variety, namely ROK3 (Ngɛyima yar-kay – Mende), was discovered by the research station from the farmers' fields (Richards, 1985). ROK3 was one of the favourites in the farming communities, from the research stations and the Seed Multiplication Project, that we supplied to our farmers while serving as the SLC/CCD project manager.

The importance of information management from indigenous knowledge for improving and sustaining productivity in upland rice farming in Sierra Leone cannot be over-emphasised. With time, farmers add to their stock of individual indigenous knowledge from their personal experiences and those gained from other farmers within and outside their farming communities. However, the lack of an earlier meaningful intervention programme during the colonial period to introduce scientific studies in the form of ethnoscience, which would have enhanced our understanding of upland rice farming, was a missed opportunity. It would have enabled farmers to gain some form of the western models of scientific enquiry, understanding and interpretations to add to their existing systems of generating indigenous knowledge for needful collaborative research on information management.

The problem with the indigenous knowledge in upland rice farming in Sierra Leone is that it is held in memory and cognition by the heads of the older farmers who do not have the means and capacity for documentation. In most cases, the initiation ceremonies served as the media of information transfers through oral instruction and demonstration. With the introduction of western education, the farmers in the rural communities were unable to continue using their traditional methods of passing their knowledge on to their posterity as they used to do in the past during their year-long initiation ceremonies. The reason is that there is hardly any time available for any form of 'traditional pedagogue' during the cultural initiations nowadays because children and young adults have to return to their schools and colleges to avoid missing out on their education. Sadly, as the old farmers die, their wealth of indigenous knowledge is lost. This was the case during the years of fighting and rebel incursions in the 1990s that claimed so many lives and devastated the rural areas, the predominantly rice-farming communities.

Many debates and published literature on indigenous knowledge in African farming systems tend to pay greater attention to merely acknowledging its existence than its usage by farmers, extension services, and researchers. This

20

book intends to highlight the indigenous knowledge in traditional upland rice farming in the West African state of Sierra Leone and how the farmers use it in information management.

With a consensus ideological approach on how we use indigenous knowledge in information management among farmers and professionals, they can influence policymakers to formulate appropriate intervention strategies for its use to increase productivity. It will make it possible to tap into indigenous knowledge to obtain information for its management as a factor of production, backed up by well-coordinated research and advisory extension services.

With the increasing demand for more radical changes for human activities to be greener on consumerism, the importance of promoting environmentally friendly farming practices as those in upland rice farming could be the assurance for the attainment of sustainable agricultural development goals in Sierra Leone. The starting point for all professionals is to understand indigenous knowledge on traditional upland rice farming and how to use it to increase productivity, aiming to facilitate its wider dissemination and application for all the farming communities in the country.

In the paper: 'Local and Farmers' knowledge matters! How integrating informal and formal knowledge enhances sustainable and resilient agriculture,' the Journal of Rural Studies (April 2018), with prudent acknowledgement, stressed the significance of indigenous knowledge, referred to as "local knowledge" in farming and sustainable agricultural development. The paper highlighted that:

- Sustainable and resilient agriculture is knowledge-intensive and requires location-specific knowledge.
- Farmers rely considerably on informal knowledge and learning modes.
- Local farmers' knowledge strengthens sustainability and resilience yet remains undervalued.
- Knowledge networking and transdisciplinary facilitate the integration of diverse knowledge.

The abstract highlighted that the widespread transformations in farming practices in recent decades across many parts of Europe have involved increased capital intensity, scale enlargement, specialisation, intensification of the usage of hybrids, increasing soil fertility, and mechanisation. These transformations in farming practices have been accompanied by quite a dramatic shift towards more standardised agricultural knowledge and information management. It goes on to state that previous research reveals that the transition towards more sustainable agriculture requires a new knowledge base, with new content and forms of knowledge, together with new processes of learning. The paper explores the relevance of informal farmers' knowledge and learning practices in constructing alternative pathways to sustainable agriculture and strengthening agricultural resilience.

Based on eleven case studies in the international research programme RETHINK, the paper revealed the diversity of knowledge sources and learning forms that farmers use and the particular role of farmers' experience-based knowledge. It also revealed that farmers greatly value local experiential knowledge as they see it as having practical, personal and local relevance.

Given the limitations of standardised information and knowledge and the urgent need for a transition towards more sustainable and resource-efficient practices, the paper argues that the potential of local farmers' knowledge is not being used optimally and that better integration of various forms of knowledge is needed. The authors identified several ways of integrating the different kinds of knowledge. For the individual farmer, it can be done by synthesising knowledge from various sources. It can also be done through farmers' networking (whether or not facilitated by formal agricultural knowledge institutions), by collaboration between farmers and researchers as knowledge co-generators, and through multi-actor knowledge networks that bring together participants from various fields. The authors concluded that the dynamic contexts, complexity and local specificity of the current challenges facing agriculture and the many roles it is expected to fulfil, require more inclusive, flexible modes of governing the generation, integration and sharing of knowledge.

Increasing small farmers' productivity is no substitute for large-scale commercial rice farming geared toward boosting agricultural productivity and vice versa. Essentially, they should be running side by side and interlinking where necessary for the overall production in the country. All stakeholders, including farmers, need recognition as equal co-authors of knowledge generation, and all kinds of knowledge, both formal and informal, need to be brought together in innovative ways.

Knowledge networking, including multi-actor knowledge Knowledge networking, including multi-actor knowledge networks that facilitate knowledge exchanges, joint learning and the generation of new and more integrated solutions, is crucial for agriculture to be sustainable and resilient (The Journal of Rural Studies, Vol. 59, April 2018; pages 242–251).

The UN Food Systems Summit, held during the UN General Assembly in New York on the 23rd of September, 2021, sets the stage for global food systems transformation to achieve sustainable development goals by 2030. To achieve sustainable agricultural development in Sierra Leone there has to be a foundation engendered by the formulation and implementation of appropriate government policies aimed at the timely supply of inputs such as tools, seeds, and extension services for farmers to increase their productivity. In line with the timely supply of farm inputs, there is the combination of the essential agricultural development factors, including information management, the availability of arable land, labour and labour-saving devices, with adequate and appropriate storage facilities for managing post-harvest losses. Above all, there should be available and easily accessible transportation with marketing facilities and favourable pricing policies for their farm produce, serving as incentives and encouragement for farmers to increase and maintain their productivity.

Chapter One

Upland Rice Farming in Sierra Leone: Indigenous Knowledge and Practices

Sierra Leone lies on the west coast of Africa, with an area of 27,928 square miles and a population of about 8 to 8.5 million people (World bank/Worldometers March 2022). It is bounded by Guinea, in the north and Liberia, in the southeast (Plate 1). The ten-degree north line of latitude forms part of the interterritorial boundary with Guinea, and it is the most northerly latitude reached. In the south, part of the boundary with Liberia is the Mano River, which extends to the sea at the 60-degree north line of the closest latitude. It is bounded in the western area by the Atlantic Ocean.

Sierra Leone extends as far west as the 13-degree west meridian and goes as far east as the 10-degree west meridian. The coastline is approximately 200 miles long and projects into a convex bulge towards the sea. It runs from northwest to southeast in that direction.

Sierra Leone is about 180 miles across and is roughly circular, divided into four regions of Northern, Eastern, and Southern Provinces and the Western area comprising the capital city, Freetown, and its environs (Plate 2).

Plate 1: Sierra Leone on the map of West Africa

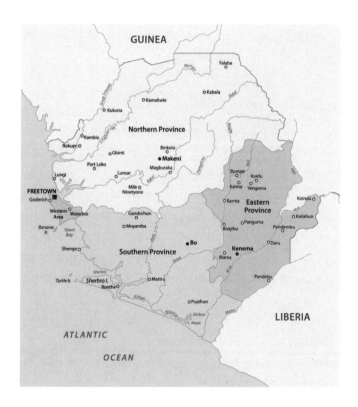

Plate 2: Sierra Leone with the provincial divisions and the western area.

The Natural Vegetation

The natural vegetation in Sierra Leone comprises tropical rainforests and semi-deciduous forests. Tropical rainforests are predominantly in the eastern and western areas (Saville and Fox 1967). The rainforests are composed of lianes and woody and herbaceous epiphytes, rich with a combination of many different plant species, most of which are well-known to farmers as soil fertility indicators for growing rice.

Semi-deciduous forests are predominantly in the north, centre, and southern regions (Saville and Fox, 1967). Although similar to Tropical Rainforests, they are dominated by deciduous trees wherein the undergrowth remains evergreen with fewer species than in the Rain Forest. The relative humidity is low in the dry season, with rainfalls lasting only two months in some seasons. There have been noticeable variations in the intensity and duration of the rainy season, nowadays, years primarily resulting from global warming, as witnessed in other parts of the world. Upland rice farmers in the Eastern Province also practice plantation agriculture (coffee and cacao).

Rice Farming in Sierra Leone

Sierra Leone is one of the rice-producing and consuming countries in West Africa. Rice is the staple food of Sierra Leoneans, cultivated in upland farming, swampland, boli, riverain and grassland ecologies. Upland rice farming is the main occupation of the rural communities. Seasonal rainfalls are the sole means of irrigation for rice cultivation in the country. Subsistence farming dominates, wherein the farmer grows food only to feed the family. Surplus production is often planned for sale in the market to meet anticipated expenses such as paying school fees for the children, initiating the children in the cultural societies or paying a bride price.

Upland rice farming is one of the oldest farming systems in Sierra Leone and remains the primary source of food production for the rural areas. It has been featured consistently as a significant agricultural policy matter in the country since the colonial period. During the colonial era, the government earned a high percentage of its foreign exchange by exporting palm oil from processing fruits collected from wild oil palm trees, coupled with the foreign exchange earned from the export of timber, also a product from the forests (Richards, 1985). As a result, upland rice farming was frowned upon with disapproval as one of the activities of the indigenous people that posed threats to the economic interest of the colonial government. Upland rice farming was regarded as a practice that caused the depletion of the population of wild palm trees and caused deforestation. The colonial government maintained that wild oil palm trees and timber were, indiscriminately destroyed in land clearing. Without fire belts when clearing the forest before burning, the adjacent forest is unintentionally consumed by the fire therein destroying the wild palm trees and timber.

To protect the government's interest, the administration launched a nationwide campaign to dissuade farmers from practising upland rice farming. The government promoted swamp rice farming as the alternative means of rice farming using the premise that it produced, comparatively, more yields per acre (Richards, 1985).

In the attempt to promote swamp rice farming on a large scale, the activities of the Rice Research Station in Rokupr were concentrated on swamp rice cultivation, even though the dominant rice farming in the country is that on the upland. This policy approach, laden with intentional bias, consequently put upland rice farming in an unfavourable position with the administration. This was a time when appropriate policies and research could have unveiled ways that would have led to unlocking the full potential of this farming system.

Despite the lack of interventional improvements in the practices, upland rice farming has remained resilient and environmentally friendly. Unfortunately, the lack of the necessary professional interventions in upland rice farming has rendered it inadequate in maintaining the food supplies of the increasing rural population, let alone meeting the food demands of the nation.

Upland rice farmers only produce rice in the swamp (as a second farm for the women) for sale to earn cash income if time permits and when they can afford the extra labour. The fact remains that rice farmers prefer the taste of upland rice varieties to swamp rice varieties.

There is a common saying among the natives that it is disrespectful and self-defeatist for a farmer to offer rice produced in the swamp as a gift to his mother-in-law (held highly within the customary tradition). The reason is that the farmer would not want swamp rice for their consumption because it lacks the desirable taste. As a result, the gesture is seen as though it is a way of disposing of what is undesirable.

The taste of the rice variety is of particular importance to the women due to the responsibility of preparing meals for the family, visitors and strangers. They know that rice without the desired taste requires far more delicious sauce to go with it to make it palatable than tasty rice. Besides, they cannot always afford the condiments for preparing delicious sauces to compensate for the lack of taste in the rice. Rice with the desired taste only needs a touch of palm oil and pepper to make it palatable for the farm family in times of scarcity.

Unlike swamp rice cultivation, upland rice farming has the advantage of intercropping. In intercropping, the farmer sows the varieties of rice seeds on different portions of the farmland, each rice variety mixed with cereal and vegetable seeds. The women sell part of the cereals and vegetables after harvest to earn cash for the family.

Without due recognition of these merits, the replacement policy of upland rice farming with swamp rice farming by the colonial government gained popularity and welcomed support from the international research centres around West Africa and other development agencies, including the World Bank and the United Nations Food and Agricultural Organisation (Richards, 1985). They argued that traditional upland rice farming was backward, lacking innovation and out of touch with the realities of modernisation with all the prospects of intensive farming techniques. As such, the standpoint was that upland rice farming lacked the capacity and capability to meet the increasing demands for rice supplies in the country.

The professionals and government authorities envisaged that the Green Revolution packages, which became very popular in the 1970s and 1980s, could be diffused more easily, in the farming communities via swamp rice farming. The mounting argument against its sustainability, fuelled by the continuous reduction in the fallow period resulting from the increasing pressure on the available land with the growing farming population, did not alleviate the bias against upland rice farming.

Despite the efforts to dissuade farmers, upland rice farming remains the preferred rice-producing system in the country. The replacement of upland rice farming with swamp rice farming was in sharp contrast with the desires, aims and objectives of the vast majority of rice-producing and consuming farmers in the country (Richards, 1985).

Even though the government was not particularly keen on promoting upland rice farming in the colonial era, as stated above, some systematic studies started during the colonial period (Glanville, 1933, 1938; Little, 1951; Jordan, 1954). These studies showed the significance of upland rice farming among experts, academics and professionals. With the strong influence of O.T. Faulker, director by then of the Nigerian Department of Agriculture, the 1948 Annual Report of the Agriculture Department in Sierra Leone noted that shifting cultivation in upland rice farming was a concession to the nature of African soils. During this period, there were other significant studies by agricultural scientists, especially at the Njala University College in the Southern Province.

"Two populist initiatives from the colonial period deserve special notice. A vocabulary of local plant names in Sierra Leonean languages, compiled over many years by F.C. Deighton, the Njala plant pathologist, was reported to be complete in manuscript form though not published until eight years later. This has since proved to be invaluable to field workers interested in Sierra Leonean farming systems. The second initiative concerns the work on indigenous principles of upland use, undertaken by the Njala soil chemist H.W. Douglas, who worked on bush burning in upland rice farming" (Richards, 1985, pg.32).

A major government intervention to increase rice production was the introduction of the Southern Grassland Mechanical Rice Producing Scheme in the Pujehun District in 1949. This scheme intended to change the existing farming system by establishing mechanised rice production in an area of about 60,000 acres. The intention was to utilise existing hamlets and villages as nuclei for plough sites on the grassland parallel to the southern coastline along the Sewa, Wanja and Marlen rivers (Richards, 1985).

According to records, Sierra Leone's economy grew by an average rate of 4.0 per cent per year from the 1960s to the 1970s. During this period, Sierra Leone was a major exporter of rice. This signifies the link between self-sufficiency in rice supplies and economic growth in the country. In the 1978/79 period, there was a depression in rice yields in Sierra Leone due to unfavourable weather conditions. To prevent such an occurrence in the future, the Ministry of Agriculture and Forestry formulated a 'Crash Rice' programme in the early 1980s with the long-term objective of increasing rice production through improved small farmers' productivity. In the Pujehun district, the programme was for cultivating 24,000 acres of riverain ecology, using tractors, power tillers, improved seed varieties, fertilisers, extension advice and crop protection (Richards, 1985). This approach to optimise rice production by introducing external inputs in the post-colonial era once again brought traditional indigenous knowledge, methods, and techniques into question.

With the increasing demand for food supplies due to the growing population in the country, indigenous practices, primarily based on local traditions, were rendered inadequate in meeting the food needs of the entire population. It brought about an increasing shift of emphasis on the transfer of technology. This time around, the alternative was not swamp-rice farming but the use of improved high-yielding varieties, technology and mechanisation for intensive production. Farm mechanisation was to help solve the problem of labour shortages for the intended intensive farming programme, expected to alleviate the bottleneck in increasing rice production in the country. The approach, however, led to the beginning of the gradual disappearance of numerous indigenous resources, including the knowledge relating to local farming practices and natural resource management. However, in the 1980s, the government was constrained by the problem of foreign exchange for purchasing requisite external inputs, coupled with the cost of maintenance of the farm machinery. As a result, the government began to seek alternatives and low-cost measures, yet again, to address the problem of food supplies in the country. It reverted to exploring the possibility of using local resources, including farmers' indigenous knowledge.

Upland rice farming is a farming system in the country wherein farmers have continued to use their indigenous knowledge with low external inputs. The external inputs comprised improved seed varieties from research stations, introduced to the farming communities by extension workers or innovative farmers. Richards (1985) stated that it sometimes appears that innovations and ecological adaptations in African agriculture are at their most vigorous where external agencies have interfered least. If this is anything to go by, it stands to reason that innovations and ecological adaptations in upland rice farming in Sierra Leone have always been at their most vigorous owing to the low interference of external agencies.

In April 1985, the Sierra Leone cabinet approved the establishment of a National Agricultural Research Coordinating Council (NARCC). The main functions of NARCC were to:

- Provide information to the government to assist it in formulating agricultural policies.
- Manage and coordinate existing research institutions and advise the government on establishing new ones.
- Oversee agricultural training programmes in the country.
- Establish Research-Extension links, and diffuse the technological innovations.

In agricultural research, extension services and technology diffusion, the common objective in Sierra Leone since the colonial era is the transfer of packages on technology developed by agricultural research institutions to farmers to increase their food production.

A great deal of the work in the agricultural extension services in the Southern and Eastern Provinces of the country relating to upland rice farming during the late 1980s and 1990s was predominantly by Non-Governmental Organisations (NGOs). Among these, the work of the Bo-Pujehun Rural development project (with German technical assistance, GTZ) was prominent in the Southern region. The Bo-Pujehun project (GTZ) adopted the integrated rural development approach. This approach involved providing extension services in community health, education, family planning, infrastructure and agriculture. In agriculture, the Bo-Pujehun project embarked on information and technology transfer from research institutions to farmers. Improved seed varieties of seed rice were purchased from the Seed Multiplication Project in the Eastern Province and other sources around the country and either supplied or sold to farmers at cost recovery.

According to studies carried out by the Bo-Pujehun Project in the 1990s, upland rice farming remains the preferred crop farming by the majority of the farmers in Sierra Leone. This is because it provides the farming communities with their major staple food, rice, vegetables and other insurance crops. About seventy-nine per cent of the locally produced foodstuffs are from upland rice farms. Upland rice farmers continue to rely on the traditional indigenous knowledge inherited from their parents and grandparents. This is unlike their counterparts in other parts of the world who have witnessed major scientific transformations with the benefit of research, mechanisation, and improving technology, fostering intensive farming, increasing productivity and commercialisation to meet the food demands of their growing population.

An Adaptive Crops Research and Extension project (ACRE), was established at the Njala University College in the early 1980s. The main objective of the ACRE Project was to seek out and improve those crops adaptable to the local farming conditions. Many of the field activities of ACRE were agronomic. Field trials were on planting materials such as seeds, potato vines, yams, and cassava stakes obtained from the farmer's fields. The Institute of Farming Systems Research (FSR) replaced the ACRE Project. The Institute of Farming Systems Research broadened its activities beyond the agronomic work of the ACRE project to studying the local farming systems, including upland rice farming, in the region and other parts of the country.

Before the rebel war, which devastated the farming communities in Sierra Leone for most of the 1990s, The Sierra Rutile Company Ltd. in the South, in collaboration with the World Bank, initiated a Sustainable Agriculture and Village Extension Project (SAVE) in the Moyamba District. SAVE operated under CARE International, establishing linkages between the research institutions and farmers in the district. On one hand, SAVE coordinated the transfer of packages and information on technology, practices and seeds developed by the Rice Research Station in Rokupr and other research institutions in the country to the farmers. On the other hand, it monitored the performances of those packages on the farmers' fields and relayed the reports on their adaptability and integration from the farmers back to the research institutions for ongoing research and development. It also took innovation and discoveries from the farmers to the research institution for further development. In performing this dual role, SAVE developed linkages between the individual farmers and the research institutions, serving as an aid in setting the agenda for a holistic approach to research and development in traditional upland rice farming.

From my personal experience as a young adult making visitations to farms of close relatives during school holidays, coupled with further work with farmers as an extension agent and project manager in the Southern Province of the country in the 1980s/90s, I can assert that, on the whole, upland rice farmers in the country continue to rely on their collective and individual indigenous knowledge for information management on their rice farming practices. It is about time that the light is shone on upland rice farming with the emergence of interest in increasing rice production from people with the capital to invest, who may not necessarily have a background in agriculture.

Chapter Two

An Overview: General Features of Upland Rice Farming in Sierra Leone with the Trends of Transformation

Site Selection: Upland rice farming in Sierra Leone is typically a traditional farming system. The Selection of a good site is one of the skills of a well-performing farmer. Upland rice farmers have a highly developed system of classifying the soils in a way that they don't only take into account the age of the bush based on the fallow but also the soil colour and a wide range of indicator plants. A key feature of site selection is that it has to be essentially close to a stream for human habitation and the sustenance of their daily living. The reason is that the farm family spends most of their daily lives on the farm during the cropping season. Land clearing follows site selection.

Land Clearing: Land clearing involves brushing, felling, burning and removing stumps. Brushing is with the machete. After cutting down the shrub vegetation, there is tree felling with the axe. The debris is left to dry for burning.

After burning, the clearing of the farmland is done by the removal of the un-burnt debris and stumping. The stumps are piled and heaped for piecemeal burning. Most of the unburnt logs of wood are used as fuel wood on the farm or sold to earn cash income. Some are left in situ to serve as seating positions for resting during cultivation. Burning the farmland to the right measure is crucial for a successful cropping season. A poorly burnt farm brings about problems, including the requirement for additional time and labour for piecemeal burning and the preponderance of weeds in the aftermath, resulting from the consequences of unburned weed seeds. Poor burning results in the lack of fertility due to the low base-exchange for the rice crop.

Plate 3: Brushing

Plate 4: Felling

Plate 5: Burnt farmland

Building the Farm Hut: After land clearing, the farmer erects a farm hut in a suitable location on the farm plot, with a barn for storage. The farm hut provides shelter, a place for food preparation and consumption, and for carrying out tasks for daily living. It is a rendezvous for the farm family to commune during breaks from the farm tasks and a place of respite to retreat from the harsh weather conditions.

Plate 6: Building a farm-hut

Ploughing: Farmers commence ploughing with the arrival of the first heavy rainfalls. Minimum tillage is the general practice. Cultivation starts by planting tuber crops followed by broadcasting the seed rice, mixed with other seeds for intercropping and hoed into the topsoil. Intercropping is the practice of growing different crops on the same field in the same season.

Fencing: Fencing commences after sowing and planting to protect the rice crop from pests such as rodents and wild animals. The farmer sets traps at strategic parts of the fence, as pest control measures and to provide meat for the family.

Plate 7: Fencing

Weeding: Weeding commences when the rice crop produces three blades of leaves. In a system of division of labour, the women have the task of weeding whilst the men do the fencing.

Plate 8: Weeding

Bird Scaring: Bird scaring commences as the rice crop reaches maturity and continues until the harvest is over.

Harvesting and Storage: These activities end the farming calendar, which is followed by a host of seasonal festivities in the villages, with these latter stages of the farming calendar coinciding with the Christmas season and the initiation ceremonies. It is the time of abundance. Harvesting starts when the rice crop reaches maturity and has undergone some drying in the field. The essence of allowing the rice to dry on the farm is to reduce the moisture content to regulate and control the moisture build-up vis-à-vis the ensuing storage conditions.

Plate 9: Harvesting

Plate 10: Milling

Plate 11: Winnowing

Plate 12: Life at the farm hut

The Labour Force

Cultivation practices in upland rice farming require optimal use of the labour force available to the farmer. The decision on the farm size depends, to a great extent, on the labour available to the farmer. It would hardly be possible to change any cultivation practice that requires an additional labour force.

There is no industry, locally or nationally, for labour-saving devices, such as farm implements and tools. Farmers rely on manual labour provided by the farm

39

family. Organised 'communal labour' and those from friends and extended family are drawn upon, when available, at peak periods for managing labour-intensive tasks such as brushing, ploughing, and harvesting. These tasks require timeliness to be ready for the expected weather condition.

Climatic Conditions

The only source of irrigation for the rice crop in upland rice farming is seasonal rainfall. Generally, the rainy season is from May to October. The dry season is from November to April, with the harmattan, interlocking, from December to February. There are variations in these months from region to region and year to year due to global climatic changes.

The rainy season in Sierra Leone is initiated by the movement of the Inter-Tropical Front, accompanied by frequent thunderstorms with torrential showers. Heavy rainfalls are in July, August and September (Saville and Fox, 1967), concentrated in short periods of heavy rains. This short duration of heavy rains implies that the farming activities such as land clearing, ploughing and sowing have to be timely. Heavy rains and flooding have become frequent occurrences in the country, potentially leading to erosion and leaching of essential nutrients from the topsoil.

Soil Condition

Some of the soils in Sierra Leone are from granite. These are young and free-draining sand and gravel with a varying proportion of lateritic gravels. Others are from schists characterised by lateritic and gravel pans resulting from prolonged weathering. The parent materials those of the Rokel river series. In the northern and central parts of the country, the soils are pure sand and contain 'finer' materials with high fertility (Saville and Fox, 1967).

It is vital for successful upland rice farming to have the knowledge required on how to identify a suitable soil condition, from the texture and colour, in combination with knowing how to identify the fertility indicator plants in the vegetation cover, Upland rice farmers in Sierra Leone are knowledgeable about the moisture retention and Cation Exchange Capacity (CEC) of different soils and how this might affect the burning of the farmland (Richards 1985). Unland rice farmers commonly describe those types of soils as 'sweating', claiming that they hamper the spread of the fire in the burning process. The farmers also believe that they have the potential to release moisture to the rice crop.

Cation Exchange Capacity is the total capacity of the soil to hold exchangeable cations. It influences the soil's ability to hold on to essential nutrients during the cropping season to promote isomorphous substitution while providing a buffer against soil acidification. Soils with higher clay fractions tend to have a higher CEC.

The five most abundantly exchangeable cations in the soil for growing rice are calcium (Ca^{++}), magnesium (Mg^{++}), potassium (K^+), sodium (Na^+), and aluminium (A^{++}). Cations are held in the soil by negatively charged particles of clay and humus called colloids. Optimum plant growth requires a balanced supply of plant nutrients. Any excess of one element may result in an induced shortage of one or more other growth-inducing essential elements for the rice crop.

The general principle is that the growth of the plant is affected by the most limiting of the essential growth factors, which include irrigation, length of sunlight (photoperiodism), and the nutrients comprising primary macro-nutrients (nitrogen, phosphorus and potassium), secondary macro-nutrients (sulphur, magnesium and calcium) and micro-nutrients (zinc, iron, manganese, copper, boron, molybdenum and caesium).

Upland rice farmers are conscious of maintaining the balance in soil fertility along the principles of limiting factors and cation exchange capacity when they say that a 'long-fallowed farm', such as one cleared from the forest, has too much manure. With this knowledge, they pause sowing, waiting for the rains to dissolve and leach out the excess nitrates. In our interviews, farmers reported that unless they do this, the rice crop will have undesirable vegetative growth at the expense of the grain formation, meaning over-long in the stalk and foliage with only a smaller head of grain.

Grist (1975) confirms that many of the rice varieties respond undesirably to an over-supply of nitrates. The advantage is that the traditional upland rice farmers in Sierra Leone have developed skills in mapping and matching their various rice varieties to the different types of soils with the understanding of the fertility and topography in combination with the practice of, somehow, mimicking the pre-existing vegetation cover as if to maintain a similar ecological and environmental balance.

Most of the efforts of experts and agriculturists in increasing food production in Sierra Leone have focused on improving seed varieties for higher yields. Work on soil conditions generally focuses on the fertility for the respective crop. The preservation of the soil's physical properties is an area to which experts have paid little attention (Richard 1985).

Based on their knowledge of the fragility of their tropical soils, upland rice farmers in Sierra Leone are mindful of practices that will lead to adverse erosion. Stumping is minimised to leave some stumps in place to avoid too much disturbance to the soil that could lead to looseness and avoidable soil erosion.

The roots of the stumps help to hold and keep the soil around them intact during the first heavy rainfalls on the newly cultivated farm until the tilled soil settles and becomes firm. In the same vein, farmers practice 'minimum tillage', which is barely scratching the surface of the soil, during ploughing, a technique they have designed from their knowledge and experiences to preserve the soil's physical properties.

Land Tenure System

In the rural communities of Sierra Leone, the inheritance of land is usually along the lines of family ownership stemming from the ancestral generations. In the extended family system, land ownership is by the various nuclear families under the custody of the head of the extended family.

Strangers can obtain land for farming through negotiations for land leases. In those cases, payment is made to the landowners from the harvest through the head of the family. Pledges are also permissible within the Sierra Leonena customary law (Saville and Fox, 1967).

Indigenous knowledge in determining the soil fertility for the rice crop is crucial for site selection and forest reservations by upland rice farmers in the country. Therefore, the individual must have a good knowledge and understanding of the soil fertility determining indicators to make an appropriate site selection when engaging in a contract agreement to avoid bargaining for unsuitable or unproductive land. That is information that they can get through consultations with seasoned farmers.

Timeliness of Farm Operations

In western or technological societies, the devices used to tell the time are commodities which must be utilised, sold and bought. In traditional African societies, the concept of time is that it has to be created or produced. Time, as a concept, is made up or composed as much as the user wants (Mbiti 1990).

With the lack of this understanding, the view commonly shared by expatriates who work with traditional farmers in Africa is that their subsistence production is due to poor time management. The temptation is to regard the farmers as lazy idlers with so much time on their hands, which they could use in other productive cash-earning activities. This claim has been challenged as a gross distortion of the reality concerning these farmers. The fact is that they are busy throughout the cropping season, especially at times of peak farm operations such as brushing, bird scaring, and harvesting. These farmers make no provision for anything like annual leave. The reason is that they have different tasks to perform at any time of the day, all times of the season and the year. The distinctions between what constitutes work life, what is private, and domestic activities, and what is leisure generally made in western societies, are not clearly defined in traditional African societies (Mbiti, 1990, McCarthy, 1994).

Time is an essential part of any crop farming. The concepts of time reckoning and its management are fundamental to the success of the operations and events in traditional upland rice farming. When upland rice farmers reckon time, it is for concrete and specific purposes relating to their farm operations/activities and not just for its social and numerical significance. They use no watches, clocks or standard calendars. Instead of numerical calendars, farmers used what one would call 'phenomenon calendars', in which the event(s) and their occurrences or phenomena which constitute time are reckoned or considered in their relationship with the task(s) that they have in hand to perform, how and when.

Time reckoning is symbolic of the occurrence of the specific event and phenomenon associated with the task. An example is that the position of the shadow of the farm hut at various times of the day, season and year would indicate what ought to have been done or should commence, or else it would be deemed to be behind schedule.

Since time is the underpinning component of the decisions on their farm activities, the farmers do not reckon it in a vacuum. The classic example is forming the relationship between the rising of the sun and their farm activities. In their reckoning, it does not matter whether the sun rises at 5 am or 7 am. What matters is the relevance to their farming so long as the sun rises to mark the beginning of the day (Mbiti 1990). This way of reckoning time is of particular significance to the upland rice farmer during the period of bird scaring when they have to be on the farm before the break of daylight to prevent the birds from invading, ravaging and causing severe damage to their rice field, which could render all of their toils and hard labour in vain.

Using their indigenous knowledge, farmers in Sierra Leone have developed ways of reckoning time for their farm activities in resonance with the local weather and climatic conditions. They receive information from their natural environment and manage it to forecast the weather condition. This makes them more accustomed to spatial and environmental learning.

However, the point is that the effects of global warming are posing insurmountable challenges to these traditional methods used by farmers when predicting the weather conditions for them to carry out their farming activities. This problem is particularly evident in poor burning, resulting from incorrect judgments and wrong weather predictions owing to the lack of adequate information.

The New and inexperienced farmers are often vulnerable to these predicaments because they do not possess the wealth of indigenous knowledge that would enable them to make the necessary adjustments. They may lack the relevant skills to take precautionary measures in getting enough reliable information from their environment or seek help from their experienced colleagues. Not every farmer can adopt coping strategies in dealing with the unfamiliar changes in the weather conditions in ways that will enable them to cope with the seasonal changes to perform their farm operations successfully.

Trends of Transformation in Upland Rice Farming in Sierra Leone

Early upland rice farming in Sierra Leone consisted of felling patches of forest, seldom more than ten acres in extent. The 'out vegetation' was burnt, subsequently, then the ground was cultivated and the rice seed broadcasted. After the harvest, the farmland is abandoned until the next cropping season and only visited occasionally to collect vegetables and other essential crops, which have a longer growing period than the rice crop.

With the increasing farming population in the rural communities, there was a corresponding pressure on the available land for upland rice farming. Today, there is virtually no natural forest within a radius of a reasonable walking distance from the villages. Arguably, there is a negligible amount of farm bush with a twenty-year follow and much less with a fallow period of more than fifteen years (Saville and Fox, 1967).

Upland rice farming in Sierra Leone has followed a trend of transformation similar to that described by Ester Boserup in agricultural production i.e. from 'forest fallow' to 'bush fallow' in shifting cultivation. The essential feature in shifting cultivation is the temporary cultivation (mostly a few years) of clearings made in the forest, which are then allowed to develop into secondary vegetation for a substantial period while new clearings are opened up successively. The ratio between the period of cropping and the length of the fallow period during which the forest is allowed to regenerate varies a great deal (Dickenson et al., 1983).

Shifting Cultivation

Shifting cultivation is adapted to forest/bush ecology and the fragility of tropical soils. Plant nutrients in tropical ecologies are concentrated in the vegetation rather than in the soil itself. The reason is that they tend to be rapidly leached by the prevalence of heavy rainfalls. The clearing of the forest vegetation for farming breaks the cycling of plant nutrients via the roots of the forest cover back to the foliage.

Clearings in upland rice farming in Sierra Leone are invariably done manually using locally produced tools such as the machete and axe. The large tree stumps are left intact to save labour and holed the soil, while the branches and debris are burnt. The resulting ash reduces the soil acidity and makes some minerals immediately available for crop production. But the soil fertility tends to fall off rapidly, and yields in subsequent years of successive cultivations are often only half of that in the previous year.

The decline in fertility and crop yields are the main reasons for the abandonment of the farmland and the creation of a new one. Moreover, the growth of weeds may make the opening of a new clearing less laborious than the continued cultivation of the old clearing (Dickenson et al., 1983). Weeding of intercropped fields must be done carefully by hand to avoid the destruction and unnecessary uprooting of wanted plants.

In a changing world, shifting cultivation poses two challenging problems: one concerns the role of modernisation and the other concerns population growth. The challenge of modernisation is bound up with the nature of shifting cultivation itself. Generally, mechanical clearing is expensive and far beyond the means of most upland rice farmers in the country. Land clearing is with simple hand tools, including machetes and axes. Tillage and cultivation of the cleared land are by hoe in bush fallow or digging stick in the case of forest fallow. The presence of tree stumps, and roots, precludes the use of mechanised tillage, which could allow for expansion and extensive upland rice farming.

There are clear limits to the extent of the farmland by manual labour and hand tools. However, the intensification of production using mechanised clearing and ploughing is difficult, expensive and potentially disadvantageous ecologically (Dickenson et al., 1983).

Due to the force of the heavy downpour of the tropical rainfalls and the fragility of tropical soils, leaving the stumps in place helps to hold the soil structure to minimise excessive soil erosion. Contrarily, the presence of stumps does not make mechanising upland rice farming feasible at this point in time.

The problem of population growth is related to the capacity of shifting cultivation to accommodate an expanding population. Growth in the rural population implies a progressive shortening of the fallow period, which may deter the recovery of soil fertility, leading to a long-term decline in yields with diminishing returns on labour, time and other inputs.

Nowadays, upland rice farmers in Sierra Leone are accustomed to a bush fallow system of shifting cultivation with relatively short fallow periods. Notably, the argument for population pressure became tentative in the aftermath of the rebel war, which saw a significant rural-to-urban migration leaving vast forest land abandoned and uncultivated. This unintentional abandonment could have induced a form of forest fallow, a condition much more favourable for upland rice farming in the country.

Forest Fallow

In forest fallow, farmers used to slash and burn the vegetation cover. After broadcasting the seeds, digging was barely a matter of scratching the topsoil, rich in humus content from the prolonged decomposition during the long period of fallow, using the stick. During forest fallow, the trees with deep roots absorb the nutrients leached from the topsoil horizon during the cropping season through their root hairs and return them to the topsoil as they litter the ground with their foliage. The canopy formed by the forest trees suppresses the survival of weed-seeds as the fallow period gets longer. As a result, forest fallow cultivation requires less labour for ploughing and weeding compared to bush fallow.

According to Boserup (1965), rice farming in forest fallow is relatively more productive per unit area than in bush fallow in terms of output per man-hour, considering its high level of fertility and the comparatively low labour requirement for ploughing and weeding.

Bush Fallow

In bush fallow, land clearing involves brushing the vegetation and felling large trees. Deeper tillage is required to uproot the weeds, which are more likely to survive with the lack of canopy cover due to the shorter period of fallow. Weeding becomes an inevitable task with a demanding labour requirement.

In bush fallow, the period that nutrients get recycled from the deeper soil horizon to the topsoil is shorter. The trees may not have developed their roots deep enough to reach and absorb the nutrients leached by the heavy rainfalls during the previous cropping season. As a result, soil fertility in bush fallow is lower than that in forest fallow, and the yield per unit area is lower than in forest fallow.

In forest fallow, the cultivation and the fallow period are longer than in bush fallow. The transformation from forest fallow to bush fallow was an adjustment strategy by the farmers in response to the increasing demands for farmland. In bush fallow farming and all the issues with fertility and the inevitability of weeding, upland rice farmers in Sierra Leone are no longer capable of managing their land resources for optimal yields in their rice farming as in the case of intensive farming, practised in other parts of the world.

The resultant effect of the change from bush fallow to forest fallow is a cumulation of changes that occur, primarily during the rejuvenation of the vegetation that takes place when the farmland is abandoned. Firstly, many herbaceous plants, climbers, shrubs and small trees invade the area.

The razor grass (Sceleria barteri) is often common in the early stages and makes access difficult in combination with small trees, which include the following, Albizia zygia, Anthocleista spp., Cleistopholis patens, Elaesis, Funtumia spp, Harungana, Holarrhena, Musanga, Morinda, Ochthocosmus, Phyllanthus, Ricinodondron, Samanea, Trema, Xylopia spp., thereby making bush fallow cultivation a matter of necessity rather than a preference in comparison with forest cultivation which appears to be a thing of the past.

Glossary of Botanical Names and Their Relevant Equivalents in the Local Languages

(P.S. Savill & J.E.D. Fox (1967).

BOTANICAL	VERNACULAR INDEX (Key)
	Abbreviations: Creole (Cr.), Kisi (Ki.), Kono (Ko.), Koranko (kor), Loko (Lo.), Mende (Me.), Temne (Te.), Sherbro (Sh.)
Albizia zygia	**Me**. Kpakpei, or Folo-kpakpei; **Te**. Ka-Pun, Ka-Pun-Ka-yim, Ka-Pun-ka-kari; **Ki**. Kpangba, Yɛasa; **Ko**. Folo, Foo, Kpangba; **Kor**. Tungbɛnɛ; **Sh**. Pun–dɛ, Pun–ma–lɛ; **Lo**. Fufu.
Anthocleista spp	**Me**. Pɔngoi, Pɔngo–hei, Pongo–hinei; **Te**. An–kəp– kəp; **Ki**. Kpɛlɛ-kpɛlɛndo; **Ko**. Gbegbe; **Kor**. Samakombɛ, Tabakombɛ; **Sh**. Kipikiplɛ; **Lo**. Pongo.
Cleistopholis patens	**Me**. Moigbamei; **Te**. Am– Bobɔi, Am–Bok; **Ki**. Siopiando; **Ko**. Fubamano; **Kor**. Karakil–kenɛ.
Elaesis	**Me**. Torkpoi
Funtumia spp	**Me**. Boboi; **Te**. Ka–Wathia; **Ki**. Tendo (as for Holarrhena ﬂorıbunda), Wangolo; **Ko**. Bobo; **Kor**. Bandapare, Bunkankon, Poran; **Lo**. Watia.

BOTANICAL	VERNACULAR
Holarrhena floribunda	**Me**. Nunkui; **Te**. Ka–Mats; **Ki**. Tendo, Wangolo–wangolo; **Ko**. Gbasa; **Kor**. Basa, Bongakon; **Lo**. Nuku.
Musanga cecropioides	**Me**. Ngovui; **Te**. An–Fekan; **Ki**. Peindo; **Ko**. Wunsonɛ; **Kor**. Wunson **Lo**. Ngogho.
Morinda geminata	**Me**. Njasui; **Te**. KaBɔmbɔ, An–Wanda; **Ki**. Soka, Suka; **Ko**. Kandui; **Kor**. Karlulɛ; **Sh**. Gbilgbil–lɛ; **Lo**. Bɔmbɔ; **Cr**. Brumston.
Ochthocosmus africanus	**Me**. Tɔwanyɛi, Twanyɛi; **Te**. Ka-Thɔnai; **Ki**. Tundui – halo; **Ko**. Tɔwanɛ, Tuafa; **Kor**. Buwulakoloma; **Lo**. Fɛgurugoongo.

Phyllanthus discoideus	**Me**. Kɔngɔ-ijoi, Ngongo – lijoi, Tijoi; **Te**. Ka–Saka; **Ki**. Cholondo, Solondo; **Ko**. Tisoɛ, Tusuɛ; **Kor**. Yɛgerɛ; **Sh**. Nɛnkon–dɛ; **Lo**. Tihu.
Ricinodondron heudelotii	**Me**. Gbɔlei, Kpɔlei; **Te**. Ka–Kino, Ka–Sigbɔrɔ; **Ki**. Gbo, Kpo; **Ko**. Gbɔɛ, Gbwɔyɛ; **Kor**. Gborɛ
Samanea dinklagei	**Me**. Gongoi, Gungui, sungui, Ngongoi, Ngungui, Saamei; **Te**. Ka-Sinɔ; **Ki**. Tamatɔmda, Wongo; **Ko**. Ongone, Wongone; **Kor**. Sansan (as for Albizia feruginea), Wonge; **Sh**. Bonda–lɛ (as for Albizia feruginea); **Lo**. Nonge;
Trema guineensis	**Me**. Ngɔmba–wuli, Ngɔmbei; **Ki**. Samsɛlɔ; **Ko**. Ɔmba, Wɔmba; **Lo**. Ngɔmba.

In many cases, the species listed above form more or less pure stands, which may develop into forty feet high bush. If the farm was made in a dense forest, the first stage may be a pure pole crop of Musanga. A few relic trees of the original forest are usually present (Saville and Fox, 1967). Given the time to progress in the fallow, the second stage is a pole crop of potentially larger trees mainly light demanders such as Amphimas, Bombax, Bridelia, Ceiba, Chlorophora, Fagara, Nauclea, Pycnanthus, Ricinodendro, Terminalia.

BOTANICAL	**VERNACULAR**
Amphimas pterocarpoides	**Me**. Njombo–wuli; **Te**. Ka–Thanka, Ka–Thanka-ka–runi; **Ki**. Koliyombo; **Ko**. Kuiyombo; **Kor**. Kusukorɛyenkɛ.
Bombax buonopozense	**Me**. Titii, Yawumbui; **Te**. An–Folan, An–Ponk-ponk; **Ki**. Peingo; **Ko**. Fua, Fua–Kɔne, Fula; **Kor**. Disile; **Sh**. Sengben–dɛ; **Lo**. Togba; **Cr**. Rɛd–kɛntin– ri.
Bridelia spp	**Me**. Kui; **Te**. Ka–Ta; **Ki**. Sindio; **Ko**. Bembe; **Kor**. Bembɛ, Fira–bembɛ; **Sh**. Yɛki–lɛ
Ceiba pentandra	**Me**. Nguwei; **Te**. Am–Polon; **Ki**. Gbanda; **Ko**. Gbanda; **Kor**. Banda; **Sh**. Polon-dɛ; **Lo**. Ngukhɔ; **Cr**. Kɔtin–tri
Chlorophora regia	**Me**. Semei; **Te**. Ka–Thema; **Ki**. Semɔ; **Ko**. Sema; **Kor**. Semɛ; **Lo**. Heiwa; **Cr**. Iroko, Kitima.

Fagara spp	**Me**. So–wuli, Fui, Makui; **Te**. Am–Bek; **Ki**. Bakio; **Ko**. Kpaikine; **Kor**. Wea.
Nauclea vanderguchtii/diderrichii	**Me**. Bundui, Nja–bundui; **Te**. Ka–Tholəna; **Ki**. Ndundo; **Ko**. Ndundu–kaima, Yi–Ndundu; **Kor**. Yabanda– yirɛ, Yadunde; **Sh**. Gbilgbil–lɛ; **Lo**. Mbundu; **Cr**. Brumston.
Pycnanthus anglolensis	**Me**. Gbɔyɛi, Kpɔyɛi; **Te**. Ka–Wor; **Ki**. Yɔma; **Ko**. Gbɔsone, Kpɔsone; **Kor**. Gbonson; **Lo**. Kpɔhɔru.
Ricinodendron heudelotii	**Me**. Gbɔlei, Kpɔlei; **Te**. Ka–kino, Ka–Sigbɔrɔ; **Ki**. Gbo, Kpo; **Ko**. Gbɔɛ, Gbwoyei; **Kor** Gbor
Terminalia spp	**Me**. Foni–baji, Bajii, Kojaagei; **Te**. Ka–Ronko, **Ki**. Basio, Kongo; **Ko**. Gbasi, Kone; **Kor**. Wasɛ, Wo, Fira–Wase, Bese, Kumkuribe; **Lo**. Babi; **Sh**.Bak–lɛ; **Cr**. Ronko, Bich–oak.

Depending on the length of the fallow, a young secondary forest will emerge at this stage, easily recognised by the appearance of a uniform structure, with the preponderance of light demanders and the presence of oil palms. The final stage depending upon the length of time allowed results from the unequal growth rates and potentialities of the various species: Ricinodendron and Bridelia die out quite early, replaced by new species, especially shade bearers. Eventually, a heterogeneous mixture typical of high forests is brought about, more or less similar to the pre-existing primary forest according to its age (Saville and Fox, 1967).

Due to the lack of the necessary modern scientific studies and intervention to direct the course of these transformations in shifting cultivation and fallow systems, upland rice farmers have been left far too long on their own devices to invent new strategies to make the necessary adjustment in their practices. They are the experts in generating new knowledge from their experiences to update their indigenous knowledge and information management. Unfortunately, the effect of the global challenges is unprecedented, and their personal experiences used to update their indigenous knowledge to develop coping strategies are individualised and not necessarily shared for the benefit of the wider farming community.

Chapter Three

Basic Concepts in Traditional Indigenous Knowledge

Concepts are abstract units in which we think and organise our thoughts, imagination, visualisation, emotions, and feelings about people, places, things, and phenomena, to make sense of the world around us. They are inventions or constructions of ideas and understandings held in our memory (Jones, 1994). The concept of 'knowledge' is generally associated with human culture. A person's knowledge is not a random set of facts and figures. It is structured around concepts in a complex network of thoughts so that a whole mass of interconnected ideas can be retrieved from memory in the process of thinking (Garforth, 1993).

Knowledge is the body of information and familiarity with various subjects of nature and our human societies gained through learning and experiences. It is the sum of what is known to the individual (The Concise Oxford Dictionary of Current English). To know is to have a mental stock of information about someone, a group of people, something, places, subjects, concepts, discoveries and imagination of the external world.

Knowledge is the condition of knowing someone, something, and the nature of the world with a certain degree of familiarity. The state of 'knowing' is attained by receiving information from our environment and other sources through our senses, imagination, intuition, experience, instruction, studying and learning consciously or unconsciously (Weber's Third New International Dictionary).

The Universal English dictionary defines 'knowledge' as the body of information known to an individual and held in their head. The above are not exhaustive of the definitions of the concept of knowledge. Their relevance is in signifying the interrelationship between knowledge and information, which essentially forms the basis of the following discussions on indigenous knowledge

51

in traditional upland rice farming in Sierra Leone and its uses in information management. From the definitions, one can see the mutually supportive and inclusive relationship between knowledge and information, like a reciprocal interconnection. In short, we can generate information in tangible and physical forms and acquire new knowledge or update our existing knowledge from the information we receive.

In the first definition, we can see that certain aspects of knowledge as experiential. The relevance of this is that most of the indigenous knowledge associated with traditional upland rice farming is from the experiences of individuals.

The second definition shows how we acquire knowledge through instruction and study. It makes the point that knowledge is a condition of knowing, an abstract state of the human brain/mind constructed in the process of retaining what is known, with the capacity to retrieve what is known, in perceptible nature, that we can share with others in the form of information. This book discusses how farmers generate information from their knowledge of their upland rice farming practices.

The third definition takes a systemic view of knowledge, stating that although knowledge is said to belong to individuals, by using the 'system theory, it can be possible to discuss the body of knowledge commonly shared by a particular group of people in a country, region, community or location. By applying the systems theory, we can discuss the collective body of knowledge in a farming community as the indigenous knowledge of traditional upland rice farming in Sierra Leone.

Each person's knowledge of the world is personal and unique. However, people from similar backgrounds, cultures, traditions and shared experiences may acquire similar concepts and ways of thinking and behaving with similar patterns of associations and activities. This would lead to a common stock of knowledge referred to as their 'collective knowledge', which can be 'scientific knowledge' or 'traditional knowledge'.

Scientific knowledge is from experimentation, universal verification and validation. It is deduced from the reductionist theory wherein data is further broken down into elements to study their respective functions and verified with empirical evidence. Traditional indigenous knowledge is generally from intuition, experiences, and the common understanding of the beliefs, attitudes. and customs that are characteristic of the heritage of a particular group of people.

There are no structured experiments or field trials, but based upon discovery and ongoing close observations made by the individual or group over time, in ways that can satisfy them as reliable for inferences and deducing from those observations. It is holistic and constructed as a whole rather than fragments. In the case of the traditional upland rice farmers in Sierra Leone, the entirety of their world of farming and environment is the laboratory for their experiments.

Indigenous Knowledge

It is difficult to find a universally accepted definition of indigenous knowledge. This difficulty is partly due to the use of different terminologies by authors who have written about the concept. Chambers (1993), in his book Putting the last First, mentioned some of the terms and phrases that have been used and preferred "Rural People's knowledge". Richards (1985) used "People's Science" in his book Indigenous Agricultural Revolution. Other writers prefer 'Traditional Ecological knowledge' or 'Local knowledge'. These differences, only a few mentioned here, can be found in the literature about indigenous knowledge in the published literature. Each author uses the phrase that, in their view, best describes the knowledge among the rural communities, particularly in developing countries, such as that found on upland rice farming in the rural communities in Sierra Leone.

Indigenous means that it is situated and intrinsic to the place of reference and, therefore, is native to the location. In the same vein, it is possible to refer to the scientific knowledge existing in western societies as indigenous to the respective place owing to its long-standing historic situatedness with the people and easily identifiable with that location. It may have originated there or have been introduced over a long period, becoming integrated into the lifestyle, culture and identity.

One distinguishing factor is that indigenous knowledge in most of the rural communities of the developing countries has remained traditional, whilst the indigenous knowledge in the western developed countries has evolved and transformed with time resulting from scientific research, innovations and discoveries. The phrase 'traditional indigenous knowledge' will be used in this book to refer to the knowledge found among the people in the upland rice farming communities of Sierra Leone.

Traditional Indigenous Knowledge

Traditional indigenous knowledge is the combined body of knowledge found among people in a particular geographical location that was either introduced and adopted or originated from them, derived from their history, cultural practices, local customs, beliefs and attitudes. It represents their values and is the entirety of their personal and collective experiences. Traditional indigenous knowledge is transmitted and passed on through the educational processes inherent in cultural practices, customs, and social interactions. It is often retained within the community and passed on to posterity from generation to generation. It constitutes the abstraction and representation of the contextual framework, quantumness and empirical content of their shared common knowledge, which varies across space, changing with time and transferring from generation to generation through oral tradition.

General Features of Traditional Indigenous Knowledge

Traditional indigenous knowledge is generally in the form of 'working knowledge' acquired through experience, stored as knowledge retained in memory and available to the individual. In a broad sense, it is a personal mental notebook for the individual, unavailable to others until the individual shares it.

The types of knowledge found in traditional societies are generally mystical, empirical, collective, individual, tacit and symbolic. Traditional indigenous knowledge is held in memory and transmitted through oral tradition, often coded in folk stories, songs and drama. Traditional indigenous knowledge is holistic and not based on reductionism in its experimentations. It works on the premise that the components of knowledge systems are analysed in their functional inter-relations rather than fragments, fractions or isolation.

Dimensions of Traditional Indigenous Knowledge

Traditional indigenous knowledge exists in folk ecology, ethnoecology, techniques, environmental and technical knowledge. It is acquired from intuition and represents the social and spiritual understanding of the world, of which their farming practice is centre as perceived by the individual and the community.

Traditional indigenous knowledge on upland rice farming is about the entirety of the farmers' environment and their ways of life. The reason is that rice farming is central to life in those communities (Chambers, 1983). For example, before the farmer starts cultivation, they must observe the traditional practice of appeasing the ancestral spirits to bless the soil for increased productivity. This shows how indigenous knowledge embraces cultural beliefs and experiential knowledge as constituent parts. It is about incorporating all the facets, including the concrete, physical, abstract, and mystical dimensions.

The types and dimensions of traditional indigenous knowledge on upland rice farming in Sierra Leone vary from region to region, community to community, and across gender due to the gender division of labour and tasks in upland rice farming in the country.

The dimensions of traditional indigenous knowledge found in the upland rice farming communities in Sierra Leone are diverse, varied, and in a complex structure of interdisciplinary networks. Much of the traditional indigenous knowledge in farming relates beyond the productivity domain and context of their farming to incorporate the totality of life experiences shared in the community.

Understanding the varying domains of knowledge and information systems in upland rice farming practices is vital for understanding the general principle within the farming system. Traditional indigenous knowledge includes technical and various types of insights, wisdom, ideas, mystical or religious beliefs, cultural norms, institutions and knowledge about the lunar or geographical conditions (Brokensha, D. et al., 1980).

Specialised knowledge in traditional societies, such as treasured insights into soil fertility and the medicinal qualities of plants, are often kept secret and known only by a select few, including elders, midwives, healers, or in the case of farming by the older experienced farmers.

Traditional Indigenous Knowledge Systems

In systems theory, a system comprises certain identifiable interrelated elements within a boundary. The boundary gives the system structure that helps to distinguish it from others, using context and relevance to the purpose of the use, enquiry or study. A system is dynamic in that it is subject to changes when activated by the activities of the elements and components.

Traditional indigenous knowledge systems constitute elements that are constantly involved in dynamic information-related processes. In their interactions, they tend to maintain a common boundary which is permeable; that is, it allows new information to filter through and make either an addition, distortion or replacement of the existing knowledge. As a result, knowledge is not static but is constantly and actively updated by the individual, consciously or subconsciously, in the process of thinking while receiving and creating information for the individual, which they can share with others.

A knowledge system is determined and identified by the knowledge domain. A knowledge domain is a subject or topic under which specific knowledge is categorised. Within a domain are a series of knowledge systems and sub-systems. For example, within the domain of an indigenous knowledge system, it is possible to find traditional indigenous knowledge, which comprises all those knowledge-related processes in the indigenous practices. Within a system of traditional indigenous knowledge, one can also find the indigenous agricultural knowledge system.

Traditional indigenous agricultural knowledge system comprises a combination of the individual and the collective knowledge of the farmers, their traditional institutions, groups and individuals involved in the generation, utilisation, transformation and consolidation of their traditional indigenous knowledge.

There can also be sub-systems, as in the case of the indigenous knowledge system in upland rice farming, found within the indigenous agricultural knowledge systems in the farming communities in Sierra Leone.

Traditional Indigenous Knowledge Generation and Transformation

Knowledge generation involves all processes involved in producing information to update knowledge or to create new knowledge. Knowledge transformation is the individual and collective engagement to continuously and collectively change knowledge acquisition to match their changing situations, circumstances, values and customs. Agricultural researchers and extension workers should have the means of capturing the significant changes over time to advise farmers to adjust their practices correspondingly. For example, the transformation from forest fallow to bush fallow corresponds to a transformation of knowledge about land use, tools and the necessary adjustments in the practices to adapt and maintain social and economic stability in the farming communities.

Forms of Traditional Indigenous Knowledge

The various forms of traditional indigenous knowledge can be mystical or rational, empirical or conceptual, positive or speculative, collective or individual, symbolic or tangible. It can be in the form of 'perceptual knowledge' of the external world comprising space and time, universal and territorial. Traditional indigenous knowledge can be 'working knowledge' or 'technical knowledge' (Jones, 1994). Understanding the various forms of indigenous knowledge can enhance our understanding of how the farmers manage the information available to them, faced with the increasing challenges of adjusting their practices to cope with the ever-changing farming environments.

Indigenous Knowledge Utilisation

Knowledge is utilised when it is put into practical application to achieve specific desired goals and objectives. At the individual level, knowledge is utilised by upland rice farmers when they initiate a sequence of processes involving the recognition, identification and interpretations of the message(s) derived from the information they receive from their environment. With this information gathering, the farmer tries to make sense of the information through a mental assessment of the incoming information based on what they already know. This process is continued further by relating those messages to specific tasks or events on the farming calendar using their repertoire of indigenous knowledge. Thus, knowledge utilisation and information management go as a unit to enhance decision-making for the individual farmer. The farmer may decide to seek additional information by consulting other farmers and extension workers before making a final decision.

In traditional upland rice farming the depth of knowledge that the farmers possess is in the skills and techniques they have acquired to perform specific tasks on the farm. The success of the practices reflects how much indigenous knowledge the farmer has at their disposal. It also depends on how effective it has been in managing information when making decisions in planning their farm activities in the past. Brushing, for example, may seem like a simple act of cutting down the vegetation. However, their experiences have taught the farmers that it is not as simplistic as it may appear to the ordinary observer and requires skills and techniques. By careful observation, an experienced, knowledgeable farmer in indigenous farming practices can tell from which end of the bush to begin the brushing to make the task easier and save time and energy. Generally, they want the vegetation to fall away from the individual when it is cut rather than towards them so that it does not hurt them or obstruct their advancement. Experienced farmers avoid certain trees to which they can return later when they have rested and regained their energy, knowing how hard it is to cut down those sorts of trees. At the community level, indigenous knowledge of traditional upland rice farming is utilised when usable information is obtained from the existing stock of knowledge and possessed by farmers in a farming community for its wider dissemination among potential users through the existing channels.

Agricultural extension is usually heavily dependent on communication as its intervention tool (Rolling, 1988). Communication involves the conveyance of information and messages to the recipient. Traditionally, extension methods of communication entail information transfer on technology developed by research institutions to farmers by professionals serving as change agents. This process runs alongside the communication among the farmers using their networks (Engel G. H., 1989). Within the domain of the farmers' social networks lies the site for the generation, transfer, utilisation and transformation of indigenous knowledge on traditional upland rice farming. As interventionists, it is vital to understand the conceptual framework of how farmers generate basic information from indigenous knowledge on upland rice farming and transform it into manageable forms for decision-making.

Chapter Four

General Features of Indigenous Knowledge on Traditional Upland Rice Farming in Sierra Leone

Many practices in upland rice farming in Sierra Leone are part and parcel of the cultural and customary practices of the dominant natives in the indigenous society of the country. The initiation ceremonies are held in December and January after harvesting when there is little or no work on the farms. In the past, these initiations served as a cultural pedagogic space and media of education whereby the elders in the community transferred information from their indigenous knowledge and farming practices to their youth in preparing them for adulthood. Being the main occupation and the source of livelihood upland rice farming was one of the major subjects, together with other practices such as hunting and fishing.

In traditional upland rice farming, the careful timing of the different operations is the key to being a well performing-farmer. In deciding on the time to undertake any farming activity, they have to make observations of their environment for the timeliness of the operation. The following discussion will show that the indicators used by traditional upland rice farmers for the timeliness of their farm operations are mostly phenomena of nature.

Preparation of Tools

The farming calendar starts with the time for acquiring and repairing tools, namely machetes, hoes, and axes. There are frequent distinctive sounds in the surrounding bushes, like that of a blacksmith with his hammer and anvil. It is said to be produced by avian species, possibly the dove in the wide. It happens as they migrate to the surrounding bushes close to human settlements, the villages searching for water when the streams in their usual habitats dry up with the approaching dry season. The farmers interpret the sound as a warning sign to get their tools in readiness for the season's cultivation. It is a reminder to take the tools to the blacksmith for repairs.

Bush/Site Selection

While the tools are being repaired or replaced, the farmer starts the search for a suitable piece of farmland. Nowadays, a secondary bush with a long time of fallow is all that is available due to the scarcity of forest that has undergone the required fallow. Apart from the fallow period, the following plant species* are considered favourable indicators of a suitable bush in combination with other factors.

Elieses geneensis, Aningeria robusta, Anthonota macrophylla, Cleistopoholis patens, Dichrostachys glomerata, Garcinia kola, Gilbertiodendron spp., Musanga cecropioides, Octoknema borealis, Parinari excelsa, Phylanthus diocoideus, Piptadeniastrum africanun, Pycnanthus angolensis, Samanea dinklagei, Smeathmannia spp., Sterculia trangacantha, Uapaca guineensis, Xylopia aethiopica.

*Note: Botanical names given. For vernacular names, please see the following glossaries.

Farmers' Interpretations

According to the farmers, Sterialia trangacantha and Uapaca guineensis are heavy-leaf growers. During the fallow period, these trees shed their leaves (holding the nutrients), which later decompose and help to build up humus. Their understanding is in alignment with the notion of the recycling of nutrients during the fallow process. Pycanthus angolensis, Musanga cecropioides, Phyllanthus dioceideus, Sterialia trangacantha, Xylopia aerthiopica, and Cleistopholis patens, retain moisture in their roots that they slowly release to the soil during spells of moisture stress in the cropping season. Anthonotha fragrans, Dialian Guineneense, Diechrostachys glomerata, and Eliases geneensis facilitate the burning of the farm because they burn fiercely. The rooting system of Aningeria robusta pulverises the soil thereby maintaining its texture and structure.

In contrast to the above, a composition of the following plant species in the bush is considered unsuitable for the rice crop. Anisophyllae spp., Chlorophora regia, Diospyros spp., Hymenocardia spp. Mareya micrantha, Millettia spp., Ochthocosmus africanus, Pentaclethra mycrophlla, Vitex micrantha.

Farmers' Interpretations

The roots of some of these species spread widely and cover large areas of the topsoil. Their survival will not allow the rice crop enough access to the soil nutrients. Some species have roots that absorb too much moisture from the soil to compete with the rice crop in periods of moisture stress. Others do not perform well during burning causing poor burning. Generally, farmers did not show much versatility in the undesirable species as they did in the case of the desirable species. This lack of knowledge can pose problems for inexperienced farmers in avoiding unsuitable sites.

Soil Fertility Indicators

In addition to the above criteria, dark-coloured soils are signs of compost and high humus build-up in the soil. Worm casts are signs of microbial activities in the soil, which is a good sign of soil pulverisation and aeration for the rice crop. Run-off tracks are indications of well-drained soils. Upland rice farmers are conscious that soils derived from old termite heaps often differ from surrounding soils, both in nutrient and textural properties, depending on the depth of the excavation and the biological processes within the heap.

It is not unusual to find up to sixty abandoned macro-termites heaps, per hectare, on an upland rice farm in Sierra Leone (Richards 1985). Specific crops and rice varieties are grown on different allotments on the farm, with the farmer's knowledge about their suitability for those areas. It also depends on their knowledge and understanding of the criteria for matching the seeds with the nature of the soil. In contrast to dark soils in reckoning their fertility for the rice crop, red soils are undesirable. Gravelly clay soils are not suitable as they tend to get hard under dry conditions, and the hard gravel could act as an obstacle to the rooting system of the rice crop.

In addition to the above criteria, farmers have developed skills and knowledge in identifying which rice varieties are suitable for certain types of bushes. Henceforth site selection is also determined by the rice varieties the farmer wants to grow and the availability of seed rice. Men do site selection, venturing into the forest. When an individual finds a suitable plot of land, he brushes a small portion of it near the roadside to indicate his intent to serve as a sign of interest to other farmers. He also demarcates the size of the bush he wishes to cultivate for the season. After selecting the bush, the farmers wait for the corresponding signs and environmental changes to start brushing.

Brushing

Men do the brushing. Hired or organised labour is used in addition to family labour. In deciding on large-scale brushing, the farmer makes the following observations from their environment.

- Funtumia spp., Invingia gabonensis, Anthonotha macrophylla, Manihot exculentus, and Christmas trees will be in their flowering stages.
- Bombax buonopozense will be bearing fruits.
- Robusta coffee would have reached maturity and ripened.
- The stems of Samanea dinklagei will begin to crack by an explosive mechanism.
- Phyllanthus discoideus will be shedding their leaves.
- Yoyavi (vernacular-Mende) will begin to stick onto clothes, similar fabrics and the hairs of people and animals as they walk in the bushes.

Farmers' Interpretations

The interpretation of the above changes is that they occur in these plant species due to the fall in the soil's water table as the dry season approaches. In combination with the plant indicators mentioned above, the following will be observable signs for brushing to commence.

The weaverbirds will be heard more frequently in the surrounding bushes.

Footprints of people and wild animals will be seen in the swampy areas as they traverse the terrains. The leaves on the ground will sound brittle as people and animals walk on them, typically noticeable during the harmattan. By this time, the fruits of wild oil palm will begin to ripen. The ripening of wild oil palm fruits is closely associated with the first set of rainfalls.

These initial showers of rainfalls are vital to the farmers because they are said to wash away the itching materials from the surfaces of the bush, thus allowing them to brush without experiencing skin irritations. They refer to them as the 'bush washing' showers.

Practically, the technique developed by the farmers' indigenous knowledge is to make close observations to determine which direction the vegetation is most likely to fall when cut. Upon close observation, the bush will be leaning in one direction. This results from the frequent movement of the seasonal wind in that direction. This knowledge is crucial in managing the information that will assist the farmer in deciding on which direction to do the brushing.

As stated earlier, the farmer aims to ensure that the vegetation falls away from the individual when cut to avoid obstruction to their advancement or cause any accidental harm. By so doing, the task is made easy and less hazardous. The direction of the wind on the day of brushing is another major factor to be taken into account when deciding from which end to start the brushing. The idea is that the wind direction aids the vegetation to fall away from the one doing the brushing. After brushing, the next task is the felling of the large trees, which is a separate task for another day.

Felling

Ceiba pentandre would have reached its flowering stage.

Anthonotha mycrophylla will begin to bear fruits. The fruits of Bombax buonopozense begin to ripen and fall. Funtunia spp., Irvingia gabonensis begin to disperse seeds. Semanea Dinklagei, Ficus spp., Brachystegia leonensis, Spondias mombin, Cryptosepalum tetraphyllum, and Anth ostema senegalensis will begin to grow new leaves.

Men do the felling when there is a frequent inland movement of the monsoon wind (Vui – Mende). It happens at the end of the harmattan season on the standard calendar. The wind helps with felling the trees by adding force and directing them away from the individual. Felling is followed by burning.

Burning

Soils tend to be especially acid in the high rainfall districts, which explains why the upland rice farmer in Sierra Leone is always so anxious to secure a good burn. They frequently remark on the correlation between a poor burn and poor yields. Upland rice yields are often noticeably better in those parts of the farm where branches are made into bonfires heaps for piecemeal burning. Poor results on inadequately fallow farms are, more or less, attributed to the 'lightness' of the felled vegetation resulting in a poor yield of ash (Richards 1989). In deciding on when to burn, farmers make the following observations:

- Anthonota microphylla will be dispersing its seeds by 'explosive mechanism'.
- The back of the stumps in the brushed land will begin to crack and peel off.
- There will be frequent heat waves rising from the ground.
- There will be frequent occurrences of the whirlwind in the afternoon
- There will be frequent atmospheric winnowing.

Farmers' Interpretations

The whirlwind is the resultant effect of forces created by the horizontal inland movement of the monsoon wind against the vertical movement of the upward direction of the rising hot air resulting from the increasing soil temperatures. Farmers' interpretations of this phenomenon concerning their farm practice of burning are that the heat from the ground aids in igniting and maintaining the fire. The whirlwind also indicates that the chances are high for the fire to survive because of the prevailing conditions.

They start the fire from the end of the brushed land in the wind direction after assessing how it will aid the performance of the fire. The wind acts as fuel for the fire directing its movement and causing it to spread across the farmland.

Without the wind, as in the case of a windless day, burning can be a challenging operation for the farmer, running the risk of trying to make the fire spread all over the brushed area. Additionally, pockets of fire are set at strategic points to aid the spread.

Shortly after land clearing, the farmer builds a farm hut in a suitable location on the farmland, using materials from the bush, which include poles for the structure and palm fronds for the triangular-shaped thatching.

Within the farm hut, there is provision for a barn-like storage facility above the space designated for sitting, cooking and eating.

During the building of the hut, women plant tuber crops (insurance crops), including yam, cassava stakes, and potato vines, being mindful of leaving enough space for the rice crop. Ploughing and tillage follow burning and clearing.

Ploughing/Tillage

Before ploughing and sowing, the farmers make the following observations:

- Wild mushrooms (Ngɔlai) will sprout.
- Okra, Anthonotha mycrophylla, will begin to grow new leaves.
- The Cotton trees will be shedding their cotton.
- Spider webs will appear on the farmland in the morning with water droplets. It is an indication of overnight precipitation. A sign that the seeds will have enough moisture for germination.

In addition to the above observations, some experienced farmers perform germination trials with small quantities of seed rice mixed with other crops such as millet, sorghum, vegetables, and in some cases, banana suckers (because they require lots of moisture to germinate). Generally, ploughing begins with the following observations:

- First heavy rainfalls
- The first flight of termites. Termite flights are said to be triggered by the presence of dislodging water in their habitat.
- Parches of centipedes will appear in large numbers on the farmland.

Farmers' Interpretations

To the farmer, these signs indicate sufficient moisture in the soil to initial these stages in the life circles of these species. The interpretation is that there is enough moisture for the germination of the crops. The availability of labour is a determinant factor of the time for sowing and ploughing/tillage. Ploughing is with the use of organised communal labour. Communal/extended family labour is predominant for mutual assistance in the upland rice farming communities.

Sowing

For sowing, the women mix small quantities of other seeds with each variety of rice seeds available. These may include cereal seeds, such as sorghum, millet, benni (sesame) seed, sweet corn etc. Vegetable seeds, including garden eggs, pepper, tomatoes, pumpkins, cucumbers, egusi, greens, krenkren, broad beans, pigeon peas, and cowpeas. The aim is to have a balanced mixture to avoid these crops dominating and competing with the rice crop for nutrients and moisture.

The mixture of seeds is broadcast evenly over the farmland and hoed into the topsoil by minimum tillage using a small hoe, covering them with the soil. The seed rate per unit area depends on the 'tillering capacity' of the rice variety and the assessed fertility of the soil. This system of cropping is called intercropping.

In intercropping, the different varieties of crops fulfil several functions: it ensures a varied diet and a phasing out of farm tasks, the harvests of the crops and managing the labour demands throughout the year. Intercropping helps to reduce the risks from pests and diseases, serving as an insurance mechanism against total losses arising from failure in a monocropping system. It also ensures a complete ground cover at various levels of heights in such a way as to reduce the impact of the rainfalls. Thus, it reduces the risk of soil erosion (Dickenson et al., 1983). It also serves as a system of natural mulching for moisture retention within the topsoil. Intercropping is an emulation, to some extent, of the diversity of the natural vegetation that existed on the plot of land hitherto the clearing. It compensates for the disturbance in the ecosystem and the environmental changes introduced by the extensive vegetation clearance and land use.

Plate 13: Intercropped farm

Fencing

The men do the fencing to the height of about three to four feet using bush poles, branches and ropes. They set traps with strong, slender, flexible bush poles and strings made from palm fronds or wire (if they can afford it) at various points on the fence. The main pests in upland rice farming are monkeys, rodents and birds. Fencing is a crucial aspect of crop protection in traditional upland rice farming. Without fencing, the rice field is laid bare to these pests from the surrounding bush. In addition, it helps to demarcate the boundary wherein it lies on the same site with one or more other farmers' fields.

Weeding

Women weed the rice farm. Sometimes extended family members and friends join forces for mutual assistance. The extraneous materials are stacked on the stumps to rot and provide manure for the rice crop. During weeding, the women discover those crops that may have failed to germinate and then replace them. A successful weeding depends upon careful timing. For weeding, the farmers look for the following indicators.

- The stumps of Anthonotha mycrophylla will begin to grow new leaves.
- Egusi would have produced seedlings on the farm.
- Binni seedlings would have three leaves at least. Weeding should be completed before the rice crop flowers because the rice flowers will abort when disturbed by the movements of those doing the weeding.

Fencing should be completed before the seedling stage of the rice crop. The reason is that the scent produced by the rice flowers attracts rodents.

Bird Scaring

Bird scaring commences as the rice crop approaches maturity. This activity involves using slings and small stones or mud dried by the heat of the fire while the women are cooking. The dried mud scatters in the air, spreading like pellets of missiles to scare off more birds in the field than a single stone. Some skilled farmers can load the sling with more than one stone to the same effect. Bird scaring will continue until the end of harvesting.

Bird control is one of the most labour-intensive tasks in rice farming. It requires early rising. No matter how far the farm is, the farmer has to be there before daybreak when the birds, as hungry as they will be, will descend on the farm in full force to cause maximum damage.

Harvesting

At the time of harvest, the farmers select the seeds for the next season. Seed selection is before large-scale harvesting. Work carried out by F.A. Squire, an officer in the Sierra Leone Department of Agriculture (in the 1940s), in the Kenema, Kailahun and Kono Districts revealed a wide range of local rice varieties well known to the farmers and easily recognised by the farmers.

Furthermore, Squire highlighted that farmers take precautions to keep the varieties pure. Seed rice is harvested from the centre of the fields to ensure its purity with traditional plant breeding in mind. Some rice varieties are reputedly quick, some heavy-yielders, while others are pest deterrents. For example, awned rice varieties and those with long outer glumes (jaw-bone rice) tend to deter birds and other pests.

In addition to these qualities, farmers have also developed skills and knowledge in identifying varieties suitable for certain types of bushes. Breeding of the desired varieties is through mass selection, and farmers have continued adding to their stock of planting materials by selecting for such characteristics and experimenting with new or unfamiliar seeds.

Many improved varieties released by the Department of Agriculture have been absorbed into the local planting stock and sometimes modified by further selection to suit local conditions (Richards 1988).

Harvesting is by the farm family with additional communal labour using small knives to cut the panicles, i.e. single panicle hand picking. A handful of panicles are tied into sheaves and stalked on the stumps or piled in the field to be collected and transported in baskets to the farm hut for storage in the barns, where there is division-of-labour.

Before starting to harvest, the farmers make the following specific observations, Sacoglottis gabonensis, Dypetes spp., and sorghum would have reached maturity. In any case, experienced farmers harvest samples of seeds collected randomly in the field and mill to assess the percentage of whole grains recovered.

Storage

Storage is done in the barn of the farm hut initially before transporting to the village for storage in kitchen ceilings or specially built barns. The sheaves are stacked on the kitchen ceilings. The purpose of the kitchen storage is for drying to continue from the heat of the smoke when the women are cooking. The effect of the smoke also controls insect infestation during storage. The sheaves are later threshed either by foot trampling, with the mortar and pestle or stick beating, and dried in the sun for storage in large baskets, sacks or drums. Harvesting and storage are done with care to minimise post-harvest losses.

Chapter Five

The Tacit Nature of Indigenous Knowledge on Traditional Upland Rice Farming in Sierra Leone; Implications for Information Management

Knowledge management is a field that has attracted much attention both in academic and practitioner circles. A review of the literature on knowledge management reveals that the term 'knowledge' appears to be laden with a high degree of what might be called terminological ambiguity and often requires a host of adjectives to make clear sense of the usage. Most of the discourse on Knowledge Management appears to be primarily concerned with knowledge that can be captured, quantified, codified and stored, an approach more deserving of the label 'Information management' (Hildreth & Kimble, 2002)

A discussion with professor Maurice Rolls at the Agriculture and Rural Development Department, Reading University, in 1994 enlightened me, that knowledge as we understand it to be, cannot be managed. In his words, "It is held in people's heads as such we cannot see it to be able to manage it. What we see is its manifestation in the form of information." His suggestion was Information Management in its physical form instead of the abstract form of Knowledge Management.

To understand the use of indigenous knowledge on upland rice farming in 'information management', it is vital to understand its nature and the implications for codification in information technology. More importantly, it is helpful to clarify how and where it sits in the ambiguity of terminologies used to describe knowledge.

Like the term 'Indigenous knowledge', different researchers and practitioners use varying terms to distinguish between the types of knowledge of their interest according to their views in the discourse on the subject. Some authors see knowledge and information as a dichotomy (Hildreth and Kimble

70

2002). Conklin (1996) uses the terms formal and informal knowledge. He describes 'formal knowledge' as information in books, manuals and documentation, stating that 'formal knowledge' is from 'informal knowledge' (Conklin, 1996). Rulke, Zaheer and Anderson (1998) focus on the collective knowledge of organisations, and the wider community, which they refer to as "transactive knowledge" (knowing what you know) and resource knowledge (i.e. knowing who knows what).

Similarly, Kogut and Zander (1992) differentiated information and know-how, while Seely Brown and Duguid (1998) made the distinction between 'know-how' and 'know-what' by arguing that an organisation's knowledge, which constitutes 'core competency', is more than 'know-what'. It entails 'explicit knowledge', which may be shared by several people and agencies. A core competency requires the more elusive 'know-how', the ability to put 'know-what' into practice (Seely Brown & Duguid, 1998, p91).

In contrast, Leonard and Sensiper (1998) describe knowledge and information not as a dichotomy but as concepts on the same continuum. For them, knowledge exists on a spectrum. At one extreme, it is almost tacit (semiconscious) and unconscious knowledge held in peoples' heads. At the other end of the spectrum, knowledge is explicit, codified, structured and accessible to people other than the individuals originating, generating and holding it in their heads. There are also arguments that most knowledge exists between the extremes.

Among the various terms used to describe the different forms of knowledge, perhaps the most contentious is the distinction between tacit and explicit knowledge. Taking a simple 'dictionary definition', tacit knowledge is the form of knowledge others can understand without being openly expressed; it is unvoiced and unspoken. An example might be the knowledge that a native speaker has of a language. Explicit knowledge, on the other hand, is expressed clearly, leaving nothing implied. An example might be knowledge transmitted to others through symbols, codes and signs, spoken and sign language, books, manuals, specifications, regulations, rules, and procedures.

Explicit elements are objective, rational and created in the 'there and then', while the tacit elements are subjective, experiential and exist in the 'here and now' (Leonard & Sensiper 1998, p113). Despite asserting that it is a continuum, Leonard and Sensiper still place certain types of knowledge at the ends of the spectrum and portray them as either tacit or explicit.

Brown and Duguid (1998) state that 'know-what' is explicit knowledge. However, know-how can also have implicit components. For example, procedures are codified forms of 'know-how' to guide people in performing a specific task.

This problematical distinction between tacit and explicit continues to dog much of the literature and discourse on knowledge management (Hildreth & Kimble, 2002). Many authors argue that to be managed, something has to be in physical form, quantified, countable, articulated and measured (Glaze, 1998). As a result, approaches to knowledge management have tended to concentrate on attempts at capturing and controlling what is said to be 'structured knowledge' (Hildreth & Kimble, 2002). In that vein, there is the recognition that certain types of knowledge cannot be captured, quantified, codified or stored in physical forms.

The increasing trend rides on the thinking that there are aspects of knowledge broadly referred to as 'what people know', situated in their heads, which cannot be made tangible, captured, articulated, codified, and stored. It is more or less referred to as 'less structured knowledge' to differentiate it from the codifiable 'structured knowledge' that was the focus of earlier knowledge management approaches.

The predominant approach to this form of knowledge management remains to try to convert it to tangible forms, applicable to the traditional management approach (Hildreth & Kimble, 2002). In this trend, knowledge management progressed to an extension of what is known as Artificial Intelligence, which takes us to where knowledge becomes a source of generating information: a commodity that can be codified, stored and transmitted.

With Information Technology (IT), there are tools to capture knowledge on information gargets. The 'capture' approach continued emphasising the capture of the 'what is known' into databases, manuals, books and reports and then sharing it in usable forms. It focuses on managing so-called 'knowledge assets', that are tangible and could be structured and codified, as in patents, trademarks and documents.

The 'capture-codify-store' approach is technology-dominated and orientated. The most common use of technology in knowledge management is to create a repository of what can be called 'structured knowledge' (Davenport and Prusak, 1998). What is said to be Knowledge Management is simply

Information Resource Management (IRM) with a new label (Hildreth, Wright and Kimble, 1999; Kimble, 2001).

As Offsey (1997, p. 113) noted, what many software vendors tout as knowledge management systems are only existing information retrieval engines, groupware systems or document management systems with a new marketing tagline. This view of knowledge as an object continues to dominate the knowledge management field, with some researchers still viewing the capture of knowledge as the main challenge (Alavi Leidner, 1997).

The recognition that knowledge management is a 'people process' and that knowledge is not simply an object made a significant shift in the emphasis on knowledge management. With the increasing interest in the kind of knowledge that is hard to capture, some researchers, including Buckingham Shum (1998), Swan, Newell, Scarborough and Hislop (1999), point out that its management poses significant challenges and that the existing apparatus for knowledge management is not adequate. This approach led to further debates about how to describe, and theorise this kind of knowledge, generally referred to as 'tacit knowledge' (Hildreth and Kimble, 2002).

Polanyi (1967) proposed a concept of knowledge based on three main theses.

- Firstly, that true discovery cannot be accounted for by a set of articulated rules or algorithms.
- Secondly, that knowledge is public but is also personal to a large extent (i.e. it is socially constructed).
- Thirdly, the knowledge that underlies explicit knowledge is more fundamental; all knowledge is either tacit or rooted in tacit knowledge.

Tacit or implicit knowledge is that which is known but cannot be transferred explicitly in a tangible form because it has become internalised and exists in the subconscious mind. It represents a level of insight inaccessible to consciousness because it is hard to externalise; simply put, we know more than we can tell. Hence we often hear this expression; 'I cannot put it in words'.

Tacit knowledge intertwines with beliefs, thoughts, intuition, feelings, and emotions (Polanyi1967). Nonaka (1991) provides a more recent distinction between Tacit and Explicit knowledge frequently cited in the literature on 'knowledge and information management'. He explains that 'explicit knowledge' is easily expressed, captured, stored, reused, and transmitted as data

73

found in databases, books, manuals and audible messages. Nonaka sees tacit knowledge as highly personal to the individual, hard to formalise and sometimes difficult to communicate or convey to others. He argues that tacit knowledge is deeply rooted in action and the individual's commitment to a specific context.

Tacit knowledge consists partly of technical skills and mental models, beliefs and perspectives so ingrained that we take them for granted and often cannot easily articulate them (Nonaka 1991, 1998). The practice of 'minimum tillage', mentioned earlier, exemplifies how indigenous knowledge on upland rice farming is embedded in practices and only learned through observation during a practice demonstration, whereby it is made explicit. Tacit knowledge is in practice rather than being descriptive, and the implicit ties of minimum tillage with soil structure combined with the inherent labour-saving technique are all tacit.

For Nonaka, tacit and explicit knowledge are not separate but mutually complementary entities, interacting with each other in the creative activities of humans. He calls the interaction of these two forms of knowledge the knowledge conversion process. This conversion process consists of four stages: socialisation, externalisation, combination and internalisation, each working as a system.

- The socialisation stage helps to transfer tacit knowledge between individuals through observation, imitation and practice demonstration.
- The externalisation stage is initiated through dialogue or collective reflection and relies on analogy or metaphor to translate tacit knowledge into documents and procedures.
- The combination stage subsequently reconfigures bodies of explicit knowledge through sorting, adding, combining and categorising processes and spreads it throughout an organisation or community.
- Lastly, the internalisation stage translates 'explicit knowledge' into individual tacit knowledge.

In a concept that Nonaka calls the 'knowledge spiral', knowledge creation and sharing become part of the organisational culture, the culture of the community, and in this case, the upland rice farming community. It is utmost to understand that effective information management is primarily at the system interfaces during the conversion process of tacit knowledge.

More likely, people are not often aware of the various types of knowledge they possess, particularly their tacit knowledge. Nonaka (1991) shows that tacit knowledge is hard to articulate, like that of a master craftsman with years of experience, who cannot say the principles behind what he knows and can only teach someone by taking them through a period of apprenticeship, unlike a teacher or lecturer who prepares notes for teaching or lecture using relevant materials.

Goguen (1997) states that people may know how to do something without the ability to articulate how they do it, often referred to as second nature. In the social sciences, it is called the "say-do problem". Such is the knowledge of riding a bicycle, tying shoelaces, speaking languages, negotiating contracts, reconciling personal differences, evaluating employees and using a word processor. It becomes instinctive as we get accustomed and familiar with the practice.

Tacit knowledge exists in practices wherein people may not have the means of sharing what they know with others except through contact interactions (Hildreth & Kimble, 2002). Hildreth and Kimble state that tacit knowledge is not easily shared, and the effective transfer of tacit knowledge generally requires extensive personal contact and trust. Polanyi (1967) asserts that tacit knowledge inheres within habits and cultures manifested in practices.

By its very nature, one can infer that indigenous knowledge in upland rice farming is 'tacit knowledge' held by individuals and communities commonly embedded in their farming practices, institutions, relationships and rituals. Being tacit can pose challenges to codifying without speaking to those with the knowledge and observing them in practice. Teece (1998), among others, argues that this should not be a problem and believes that tacit knowledge can be difficult to articulate but not necessarily impossible to capture and externalise.

Writers, including Huang (1997), support this premise, arguing that, although it is difficult to articulate, tacit knowledge can be captured. Nonetheless, Buckingham (1998) warns that tacit knowledge cannot be captured and codified without becoming invalid and losing its emphasis during translation. The simple understanding is what some would say, that a joke loses its fervour of humour in translation.

Indigenous knowledge in traditional upland rice farming in Sierra Leone is local knowledge and unique to the culture of the respective farming community. It is the basis for decision-making and problem-solving in areas including, but not limited to, agriculture, health care, food preparation, information sharing and natural resource management in the respective indigenous communities.

From the previous sections of this book, the assertion is that the nature of indigenous knowledge on upland rice farming is predominantly tacit, held in the individual's head. It is vital to have this understanding as a prerequisite in any attempts at obtaining and using information derived from farmers' indigenous knowledge to enhance its effective management in promoting upland rice farming.

Nonaka (1991) suggests that sharing tacit knowledge is through joint activities and requires physical proximity. He states that for others to understand what it is, tacit knowledge has to be externalised. In traditional upland rice farming, communal labour at peak-labour periods, such as brushing, ploughing, sowing, and harvesting, is the opportunity and practicum for exchanging and sharing tacit knowledge. An example is the practice of assessment to decide where the brushing should start while all the relevant indicators are taken into account, offering a learning opportunity, through observation, for those farmers who may not have acquired such knowledge.

The tacit knowledge predominantly found in upland rice farming is highly personal and hard to formalise. It makes it difficult to communicate or share with others. Unlike the practices in the academic fields or the scientific world, upland rice farmers will hardly see the need to announce their discoveries on their farms. Rather than sharing, they keep their innovations and discoveries to themselves, thereby adding to their indigenous knowledge. Subjective insights, intuitions and hunches fall into this category of knowledge. It is deeply rooted in the individuals' farming practices and the ideals, values and emotions inherent in those practices that they embrace. For example, before the traditional farmer starts farming, they perform certain traditional ceremonies to invoke ancestral spiritual intervention for a successful farming season. It is a practice with a personal quality, which is hard to formalise with a convincing scientific and logical explanation and to communicate externally. It indwells in a comprehensive cognisance of the individual farmer's unique ancestry. Although the practice is appeasement for increasing productivity as the primary aim, the underlying belief is the essence of prayerfully appealing for good wishes and the prevention of ill luck, ill health or any form of setback and misfortune that could befall the farmer, becoming an impediment to the successful completion of the farming season.

There could be an unexplained element of religious undertone to the superficial ancestral appeasement. Nonetheless, the combination of the underpinning tacit knowledge will make sense to the farmer even though it may appear irrational and meaningless to the observer questioning its relevance and what it does for productivity.

The missing link, however, is sharing the inherent spiritual context and the holistic understanding of what it means to the farming community. While farmers who observe the practice may do so from their knowledge, beliefs, and heritage, others lacking intrinsic insight may only understand it as a mere practice that ends in fulfilling what has become a requirement of the events of the farming calendar.

There are two dimensions to tacit knowledge of upland rice farming. These are the technical dimension, which encompasses the kind of informal personal skills of the farmer, often referred to as 'know-how' and the cognitive dimensions consisting of the beliefs, ideals, values, schemata and mental models held by individuals. Even though it is difficult to articulate, the cognitive aspect of their tacit knowledge shapes how the farmer perceives their world of farming.

The process of transforming tacit knowledge into explicit knowledge is codification or articulation. However, there are arguments that the tacit nature of knowledge makes it hard to codify and can be transmitted only via training, practice learning or gained through personal experiences.

Alternatively, tacit knowledge is understood to be knowledge embedded in the culture, for instance, a regional and organisational or social culture, and hardly shared with people who are not part of that culture. The kind of knowledge acquired on the ethics, codes and conduct and the expected behaviours of the society is not taught but learned in our day-to-day lives by living in the community.

Tacit knowledge is the aspect of 'know-how' as opposed to 'know-what' [facts], 'know-why' [science] and 'know-who' [networking]. It involves learning and acquiring skills but not in a way that people can easily put in writing, without subject interpretation and risk of losing its meaning in transition and translation (Wikipedia 2007).

Tacit knowledge may appear to be a simple idea, yet its implications are intricate and far-reaching in using it effectively in information management. If knowledge of such significance is tacit, it poses challenges for it to be tapped into and spreading it across the wider farming community or geographical boundaries. It means that information on this kind of knowledge will not be able to reach those who need it without direct face-to-face contact. It also means that training newcomers can be more time-consuming because they must be allowed time to learn while observing and doing, which could reduce overall efficiency and efficacy.

To collectivise and spread tacit knowledge, organisations and communities must invest in the human capital of their members. In the case of upland rice farming, information transfer and knowledge acquisition lie primarily at the farm level (the farm family) and sometimes at the village level through interactive observation and experiential learning. Simply put, for upland rice farmers, informal practice learning exists among and between individuals in the practice setting (their farms) and within their community of farmers' practice or through problem-solving.

Tacit knowledge is crucial to innovation in many walks of life. A society's ability to innovate depends on its level of tacit knowledge of how to innovate. Nonaka and Takeuchi's book, The Knowledge-Creating Company (1995), brought the concept of tacit knowledge into the realm of corporate innovation. They suggest that Japanese companies are more innovative because they can successfully collectivise individual tacit knowledge to that of the firm. Some writers on the subject infer that most laboratory practices that are vital to the successful reproduction of a scientific experiment are tacit (Collins, 2001).

In traditional upland rice farming, careful timing of the different farming operations is the key to a successful farming season. To make the right decision on the time to carry out any of the farm operations, the farmer must have acquired the requisite tacit knowledge; 'know what' (what they have to observe from their environment as indicators based on what they know), in conjunction with the 'know how' (how to relate and apply the information that they generated from that observation to the particular farm operation. It has to be said therefore that for generations, the communities' abilities for innovations in information management in upland rice farming in Sierra Leone are inherent in their tacit knowledge of what they have to look out for, how, where, and when to inform and guide their practices.

The pace of Information management helps farmers make informed decisions on performing the tasks in their farming practices. Information technological development offers the possibility and perfect opportunity for using indigenous knowledge on upland rice farming in diverse ways in information management geared towards increasing farmers' productivity.

Information management in upland rice farming is lagging behind other knowledge systems used in information management for its efficiency and effectiveness in this day and age of advancement in information technology. Recognising the tacit nature of indigenous knowledge is key to managing information derived from knowledge in traditional upland rice farming. Despite the tacit nature of indigenous knowledge in traditional upland rice farming, it has been shown in this book that it can be codified as 'basic data', transformed into 'data message', which can be structured and articulated for usage in information management tools. What is required is a robust methodology to capture the inherent information.

Chapter Six

Knowledge and Information Management

Knowledge is inherent in people as an abstract component contained in their brains. It cannot be transferred in physical form from person to person. We can, however, out of what we know, produce information that we can communicate to others. How that information is received and interpreted with the desired effect will vary from person to person and depends on its content and delivery.

From our existing knowledge, we can use words, symbols, signs and actions to communicate information generated from the ideas and thoughts we have in our head to convey our messages to others through language. This process of transferring information to others also depends on our memory structure. With our memory (storage of knowledge), we can process information generated from what we know about things, subjects, places and people. Our memory allows us to recollect and retrieve information and compare incoming information with what is known. Without memory, we cannot remember things, let alone identify them. Our existing knowledge structure helps us to interpret incoming information. In the interpretation of information, we also make use of our sensory organs. Our feelings, imagination of things, experiences, expectations, ambiguity, perceptions and many other factors play critical roles in the interpretation of the information that we receive.

Our existing knowledge enables us to assess whether the information is new, relevant, controversial, contradictory, logical, unfamiliar, acceptable or unacceptable. It helps us decide how to make use of incoming information. In the process, our knowledge becomes updated with the incoming information, which can reinforce our thoughts and notions, distorting or replacing them. Hence controversies and forgetfulness are part of human nature (Garforth, 1993). This mutually co-producing interconnection of information makes it feasible to use indigenous knowledge of traditional upland rice farming in information management.

Information is a set of data articulated to acquire meaning for the receiver. The data are in meaningful bits and pieces. The information produced is transformed into symbols, signs, words, spoken or written. If the data or the bits of information they carry are not sufficient to convey the meaning intended by the producer, there is the tendency that the receiver may fill in the gaps by drawing from their knowledge, experiences and imagination. In such an event, the chances of misinterpretation and misunderstanding are great. It is, therefore necessary to give as much information as possible and use the right kind of data in information production. Even when the information is right its management as a conscious resource is vital for the effective transfer, interpretation and understanding of the recipient (Rolling, 1989).

There is an increasing and recognisable interest in the concept of information management in many parts of the world as a vital factor of agricultural production, in combination with the traditionally acknowledged factors of production, such as land, labour, capital, planting materials and machinery to cope with the ever-increasing demand for food production.

Information Management

Information management is the application of the principles and functions of management to 'information data' intended to convey a particular message. Data are 'raw' facts and figures available to a person or group of people in generating information. They form the basic building blocks or units, which need to be processed to acquire meaning. As individual units, they can be vague and meaningless in the sense of conveying the intended message to the receiver. It is the producer and the receiver who gives the intended meaning to them. For the latter, it depends on their interpretation of what they receive.

Our knowledge of the topic enables us to present the data in a coherent and meaningful form for the receiver. Similarly, that knowledge also helps us to interpret the information we receive through our senses (Rolling, 1989). In the case of traditional upland rice farmers, the interactions with their environment hold the cues, symbols and signals for the relevant 'data' information that they interpret based on what they know.

The main objective of information management should be to make relevant information readily available to the users. This requires careful planning and deciding what information to acquire, how much, when, and where to store it to make it easily accessible to the users. There is also the need for control mechanisms to prevent misleading information from filtering through and causing misinformation. All of these components and activities entail various aspects of information management.

The changes in management practices with the development of computer technology have led to information management becoming a vital factor of agricultural production, which is now available to most farmers in developed countries. In electronics engineering, computers serve as versatile tools, rapidly analysing large quantities of data to produce useful information for management decision-making.

Decision-making takes place at every stage in upland rice farming. The right decision is determined to a greater extent by the availability of timely and adequate information. The development of linkages between farmers, extension services and research institutions has necessitated the management of information so that farmers can derive the full benefit of the information they seek and even pay for it, as is the case in parts of the developed world such as the United Kingdom, Turkey and other developed countries.

During a study tour in Turkey, as an Agricultural Extension student from The University of Reading, UK, in 1993, I discovered that the need for information is so vital to the farmers that they would prefer to pay for it through consultancy because of the insurance it offers than to use information that is given free of charge, yet unreliable and risky. This helps to demonstrate the importance of information management for the farmers, extension agents and research institutions in farming and agricultural development.

In subsistence agriculture, the farmer and the farm household are the sole decision-makers and information managers at the farm level. Apart from the long-term planning, the farmer faces the day-to-day decision-making on the events on the farming calendar coupled with the changing local, regional and global weather conditions. As a result of this and many other commitments, upland rice farmers have little or no time to seek information from sources far beyond their communities. They generally have to decide on what information they require and how much. This decision is with their working knowledge, what they already know, what they think they need to know, and where to get it. They may be aware of some sources of information but may not know about many other sources. Due to the changing situations concerning farmers, locally, regionally, nationally, and globally, they may need the necessary research and information management support mechanisms to constantly update their indigenous knowledge and adopt new information management practices.

The types of practices in information management depend to a certain extent on the nature of the information. The nature of the information, in turn, depends on the culture in which it evolves. Therefore, information produced in traditional societies differs from that produced in modern scientific societies. As such, varying adaptive methods are needed to generate, transform, integrate, consolidate, transfer, store and retrieve information within and across indigenous communities.

In developed countries, additional information is produced for farmers from experimentation and research in field trials and laboratories. It is then held on computer hardware, accessible via the internet and in books, journals, documentation centres, and audio-visual aids. This trend of managing information may involve an array of managers in various aspects at every level.

In modern societies, information is verified and presented as 'facts and figures'. In upland rice farming societies, information is predominantly from the environment and stored in memory as working knowledge, which carries the risk of forgetfulness. Trials are done inherently in the practices as often as the farmer is engaged in them.

The types of management practices in information management depend on the individual's personality. Farmers have different personalities who differ in their behaviours, goals set, and values from the so-called 'rational economic' man. These differences largely influence how they perceive, understand and collate their information. Because of the differences in individual management practices, it is vital to consider the information in indigenous knowledge, in a collective term, as an information system.

An agricultural information system is a system wherein agricultural information data are transformed, transferred, consolidated, received, and used in ways that these processes function synergistically to promote knowledge production and use (Rolling, 1989). In this concept, the institutions generating, transforming, transferring, and receiving information are as important as the information flow and linkage mechanisms between the institutions.

In the agricultural information system, the potential actors/institutions are the farmers and their communities, the extension workers and services, the researchers and research stations, the credit institutions, the traders and the consumers. Each actor is an information manager in their own right. Even though there may be similarities among the same actors sharing similar backgrounds and having the same objectives, there are diverse differences among the different categories of actors.

The information management practices by farmers may differ from those of extension workers and researchers. As a result, it is necessary to understand how the farmers structure or organise their information for any effective intervention by extension workers to support them by using their indigenous knowledge in information management for sustainable agricultural development. Farmers generally structure their information management through a pathway including a 'thought stage', 'search stage', 'gathering stage' and 'decision and action stages' (Rolls et al., 1987). These stages overlap and interlink in the day-to-day practice.

Thought stage

In the first stage, thoughts are initiated on what is happening or will happen as an event in their upland rice farming calendar. There is a mental search for information. The need for additional information might arise. The farmer anticipates tasks they need to perform and the necessary steps to accomplish the tasks.

Search stage

In the second stage, the farmer starts the search for information in addition to their working knowledge. After identifying possible sources, the farmer decides how to obtain the information needed. They decide on what type and how much is required. In the case of traditional upland rice farmers, they are often limited to those sources within their reach, such as their friends, neighbours and sometimes extension workers.

In site selection, for example, the farmer may want to save himself from going on a wide goose chase in the forest or bush. With an idea of how far they want to go from the village and in what direction, they form a mental picture of the location of his proposed farm site. Next, he ascertains whether it is part of his family bush or belongs to another family.

In their search, they effectively seek the opinion of other farmers who may have farmed in the area to find out what to expect based on their farming intent for a year's settlement. Basic daily living necessities like the proximity to the nearest stream for fetching water play a crucial role at this stage.

Gathering and Verification of Information

The third stage involves actively collecting and consolidating information from the various sources identified in the search. In upland rice farming, this is the time for consulting other farmers who may have the information. The aim is to verify and validate the information gathered. The farmer assesses the situation and potential challenges using their working indigenous knowledge. This stage involves making observations in their environmental studies for the signs associated with the intended task.

Decisions and action

The fourth stage involves making decisions and taking action. Action can be a positive or negative response to the information they have collected. Each of these stages involves one or more management practices. In this process, also several problems can converge to affect the farmer's decision-making. The ecology in which they are operating is constantly changing. The farmer may not have got information on the recent changes to help them make appropriate decisions. The climate, for example, changes due to the effects of global warming. These and many other factors contrive to affect the information management practices of farmers. Despite these constraints, their needs for information management as a full-time occupation are not always acknowledged and recognised by most professionals who work with them.

There are no written records to be found on their indigenous knowledge. As the experts in their practices, upland rice farmers are often quite willing to share their knowledge with outsiders and other farmers, provided the communication channels are available. It will allow professionals to seek their indigenous knowledge to understand the rational thinking behind farmers' beliefs and attitudes in using their indigenous knowledge in their farm practices.

In upland rice farming, the farmers generally rely on their knowledge and the information from their colleagues in decision-making on their farms more often than external sources outside their local communities. The only type of information they tend to seek from extension and other sources is on the availability of farm credits, tools and improved seed varieties. The events of the farm operations remain with them to decide.

Information management involves the production and use of information in decision-making. It means that there should be a producer and a user. In the case of traditional upland rice farming, the farmer is the producer of information and the user at the same time. Extension services in Sierra Leone have generally taken the credit and input supply approach. This being the case, upland rice farmers have always relied on their information management and are trying to adopt the techniques transferred to them by their ancestors to incorporate those from research stations. The missing link is the effective mobilisation of the information used by the farmers in decision-making and the integration of their indigenous knowledge into the extension packages. This approach can give extension workers a significant role in promoting farmers' development capabilities. It is hard to distinguish an entry point for extension and research into information management in upland rice farming. It can be suggestive, however, that the best way forward is to accept the farmers as consultants for research and development. Keep up with the farmers in the circle of farm events, beginning with what they already know, where they are at, and building on what they already have in using their indigenous knowledge on upland rice farming in information management.

Chapter Seven

Use of Indigenous Knowledge on Traditional Upland Rice Farming in Information Management

The ability to use words and signs in language to communicate in the arts of speaking and writing is unique to humans. It is man's greatest creation and invaluable asset. Language enables us to convey our myths, express our songs and perpetuate our culture. Through language, we communicate and interact with others. The ability to use language represents an enormous evolutionary step for mankind.

The key to information management is the service of language as a vehicle for communicating our thought, feeling and emotions in conveying the meaning of the information we transfer. The information contained in a language is fundamental to the viability of human society. It enables us to talk about our past, record our present, convey messages of our understanding and imagination of our world and anticipate the future (Tricker, 1982).

In recent years man's rapidly growing ability to capture, transmit, store, and retrieve data offers the potential for higher orders of human relationships between individuals, organisations and societies (Tricker 1982, p. 40). The creativity of language coupled with man's ability to innovate has opened up immense opportunities for using methods and devices in managing information in decision-making in various works of life.

The following discussion focuses on the uses of traditional indigenous knowledge in information management and how upland rice farmers might manage their information using their indigenous knowledge. It is also about how policymakers, professionals, research institutions and field workers can use indigenous knowledge for information management and farmers' advisory services.

Information management in farming can be done by an individual farmer on their farm or by farmers' advisory services, such as Farmers' Associations, Extension services and research institutions or by private and commercial services.

The main thrust of this book is to enhance the understanding of how upland rice farmers in Sierra Leone manage information in their farming system, which has remained self-sustaining with virtually low external input intervention. It should encourage agencies and the government to develop and promote farmers' information management to increase food production in the country.

Rolls et al. (1987) developed a conceptual framework indicating how farmers might manage their information. It includes models from work done with farmers in the United Kingdom, also applicable to farmers in other parts of the world, such as the upland rice farmers in Sierra Leone. From their analysis, the following are some ways farmers might manage their information.

Farm events

Upland rice farming is a seasonal operation comprising a series of farm events. The essence of timeliness is central to the performance of the events and the farming activities that take place in the farming season. The entire farming season marks the duration of the farming activities, which includes site selection, brushing, felling, burning, ploughing, sowing, weeding, fencing, bird control, harvesting, and storing. During the farming season, unanticipated problems may arise, and farmers make decisions with contingency measures to manage risks.

The climatic and weather conditions have a great deal of influence in determining when to operate for each event if permissible. The physiological changes in the plant species used by the farmers as their time indicators occur because of the changes in the climatic conditions, signalling the approaching weather. In these events, they perform tasks in congruence with anticipated outcomes.

Site selection involves searching the bush or forest for the farmland; brushing involves slashing the vegetation with machetes; land clearing entails burning and the removal of debris and logs of wood; weeding involves careful uprooting of the weeds.

To start these activities, the farmers make specific and constructive observations of their environment rather than a mere random collection of information. Farmers consciously note these environmental signs, with relevance for managing the information required to reach the decision.

Information sources

These represent the various sources from which farmers get their information and in what form and how it flows. The information sources for upland rice farmers in Sierra Leone are from their physical environment, colleagues and extension services. From the information received, they acquire personal and collective knowledge. This collective knowledge is passed from one generation to another by oral tradition.

The flow of information within the communities is through their social interactions. The nature of the information received from their environment is phenomenal and noted through their senses in the form of "basic data" and "data messages".

From their studies, Rolls, Jones and Tranter developed a concept of possible stages in which farmers might manage their information along these pathways, which include an "initial stage", "assessment stage", "decision stage", and an action stage. This concept could likewise apply to the stages in which upland rice farmers manage their information using their indigenous knowledge.

Initial stage

At this stage, the upland rice farmer develops a mental map of what observations they have to make, what stage of the season, where to look for the indicators and how to identify them when they occur. This understanding of where to search for the information will depend on the working knowledge of the individual. They look for the 'basic data' at this initial stage. With the repertoire of indigenous knowledge, the individual validates and forms an opinion about the data to give it relevance and reliability.

Using their working knowledge, the farmers will recognise the plant and animal species when they see them and can relate them to the various events in their upland rice farming. A farmer who cannot identify a species will not observe the change others see in connection with their farming activities.

Even if the farmer knows about the relationship between the species and the specific farming practice, identifying it is the starting point of the information management process.

Likewise, a farmer who only knows a species by its name and nothing more than a plant or animal cannot see and understand the meaning in the messages sent by the physiological or physical changes in that species to be able to relate them to their farming practice. All there is to know about the plants or animals and being able to identify them, what changes to look out for, and how they relate to the farm task should be in the thought process. This sequential piecing of relevant information together to make sense of it is necessary for the farmer to relate the respective information data message derived from the seasonal changes to their farming activities.

Assessment stage

Upland rice farmers use their existing knowledge to interpret the information they receive from their environment. They then assess the information gathered for its reliability and pertinence to the decision they are about to make. From their assessment, the farmers know what additional information they may require for the decision. They carry out an appraisal of the options that exist depending on the available information. Farmers also use traditional techniques such as germination trials before sowing the seeds on the farm.

Decision stage

At this stage, the farmer has to decide on the task to perform, how and when. For this purpose, they use their indigenous knowledge to make a mental map of how things should be in the face of the prevailing circumstances. They use their working knowledge to judge the content of the information collected.

Action stage

A mental decision is nothing more than a mere intent unless backed by practical implementation. Examples of some of the questions that may arise could include the following:

i. What should be the nature of the activity?
ii. Should they embark on large-scale brushing or small-scale?
iii. Should it be individual fencing or collective communal hunting activities to reduce the pest population?

Hence, information management is by stages of decision. The principles underpinning their practices manifest the depth of their indigenous knowledge and cannot be identified easily by an outside observer. For example, from their understanding, upland rice farmers can explain the roles of the wind and the hot ground in facilitating burning.

The connection between burning and the whirlwind is fascinating and shows the scientific nature of their thinking. Their interpretation is that hot air rises, thus producing a vertical force against the horizontal movement of the wind, leading to the physics of the resistivity that causes the twist and column of the whirlwind. Their analysis in relating the various components to what they need for their farmland to burn well shows that there is no lack of scientific reasoning in using this phenomenon as an indicator or part of the requirements for burning the farmland.

From their experiential knowledge, upland rice farmers can tell which rice varieties are most suitable for certain bushes and match the various seed varieties to specific locations on the farm. They can tell which side of the bush brushing should start to make the task easier.

Without the relevant indigenous knowledge required, the messages in the physical features of the vegetation will not make meaning for them to relate it to the task. This lack of understanding of the basic technique renders their information management ineffective and farming as mere guesswork.

The nature of information inherent in indigenous knowledge can be identified and categorised by the different forms in which they exist, which include 'basic data', 'data messages', and the 'information in use' (Tricker, 1982).

This section highlights that upland rice farmers receive information from their environment into 'basic data', which they transform into 'data messages'. Understanding the 'basic data', the 'data messages', and the subsequent production of 'information data' depends on the individual's knowledge of their relationships with farming activities.

Furthermore, this section shows that 'information data' and 'data messages' in traditional indigenous knowledge can be used in computer technology for information management to guide decision-making in farming and agriculture. To effectively manage information obtained from traditional indigenous knowledge, it will be necessary to understand the nature of the information data derived from it.

Basic Data

'Basic data' is the primary state in which potential information exists. They are more or less rudimentary and referred to as raw data for this analysis. Raw data are the fundamental building blocks potentially containing information to be processed. The following are some of the 'basic data' that farmers use in their information management in upland rice farming, falling under categories of phenomena, plant species, animal species, soil, and climatic conditions.

i.   Doves
ii.   Dark soils
iii.   Monsoon wind
iv.   Weaver birds
v.   Red soils
vi.   Harmattan
vii.   Spiders
viii. Clay soils
ix.   Atmospheric winnowing
x.   Termites
xi.   Gravelly soils
xii.   Whirlwind
xiii. Earthworms
xiv.   Worm casts
xv.   Run-off tracks
xvi.   Termitaria
xvii.   First seasonal rainfalls
xviii.   The lunar system

Plant species (basic data):

Glossary of botanical names and their equivalents in the local languages (P.S. Savill & J.E.D. Fox (1967). Vernacular index (Key) Abbreviations: Krio (Cr.), Kisi (Ki.), Kono (Ko.), Koranko (kor), Loko (Lo.), Mende (Me.), Temne (Te.), Sherbro (Sh).

Botanical name/Vernacular

1. Aningeria robusta: Me. Tɛyɛi (as for Chrysophyllum spp), Vao-wuli.

2. Valui Anisophyllae sppMe. Kandii, Kantii; Te. Ka – Kants; Ko. Kandi (as for Xylopia aethiopica); Kor. Kense;Sh. Kənth–lɛ; Lo. Kɛndi; Cr. Mɔki – apul.

3. Anthonota macrophylla: Me. Mbombii; Te. Ka-Par, Ka-Ponko (as for Berlinia spp); Ki. Kpɛndio Ko. Mbumbi; Kor. Bumbuse; Lo. Mbombi

4. Anthostema senegalensis: Me. Nyɛbui (as for plagiosiphon emarginatus), Sɛmi; Te. Ka-Wan; Ki. Susianchido; Kor. Famɛ; Sh. Sɛm–dɛ.

5. Bombax bunopozene: Me. Titii, Yawumbui; Te. An–Folan, An–Ponk-ponk; Ki. Peingo; Ko. Fua, Fua–Kɔne, Fula; Kor. Disile; Sh. Sengben-dɛ; Lo. Togba; Cr. Rɛd–kɔntin–tri.

6. Brachystegia leonensis: Me. Bɔjei, Gbɔjei; Te. Ka–Basam, Ka–Bi; Ki. Kondo–yulo; Kor. Mankɛ

7. Ceiba pentandre: Me. Nguwei; Te. Am–Polon; Ki. Gbanda; Ko. Gbanda; Kor. Banda; Sh. Polon–dɛ; Lo. Ngukhɔ; Cr. Kɔtin–tri.

8. Chlorophora regia: Me. Samei; Te. Ka–Thema; Ki. Semɔ; Ko. Sema; Kor. Semɛ; Lo. Heiwa; Cr. Iroko, Kitima.

9. Cleistopoholis patens.: Me. Moigbamie.; Te. Am-Bobɔi, Am-Bok; Ki. Siopiando; Ko. Fubamano Kor. Karankil-kenɛ

10. Cryptosepalum tetraphyllum: Me. Kpavii

11. Dialium guineense: Me. Mamboi, Mambui; Te. Am-Bamp; Ko. Mambui (as for D. pobeguini); Kor. Dolokɛ; Lo. Mahombo; Sh. Pimpi–lɛ; Cr. Blak–tombla, Tombla.

12. Dichrostachys glomerata.: Me. Ndandei; Te. Am-Pəntkəli; Ki. Siɛmbulo; Ko. Tasa; Kor Tansɛ; Sh. Sɛmplɛu-ɛ; Lo. Ndanda

13. Diospyros spp: Me. Ndɔku–wuli, nwanyei, Sii, T-lii; Te. Ka– Bup–ka – si, An–Gbɔka, An–Gboth; Ki. Kpililio, Pesiwe; Ko. Difin ɛ; Kor. Fira-fingɛ (as for Smeathmannia spp); Lo. Tɛi–guro; Cr. Bush-banga

14. Dypetes spp.: Me. Puje–wuli; Ko. Putu–kɔne.

15. Elieses geneensis: Me. Turkpoi.

16. Ficus spp: Me. Gɔngɔi, Gɔnwɛi, Kponi; Te. Ka–Gbono, A–kololo, An–Lop; Ki. Ndasa, Nɔngo; Ko. Nɔgɔɛ, Ponɛ; Kor. Sɛrɛ, Nonke; Sh. Rasa-lɛ; Lo. Sege–sege; Cr. Wet–wata–tik.

17. Funtunia spp.: Me. Boboi; Te. Ka – Wathia; Ki. Tendo (as for Holarrhena floribunda), Wangolo; Ko. Bobo; Kor. Bandapare, Bunkankon, Poran; Lo. Watia.

18. Garcinia kola.: Me. Sagbei (as for G. polyalthia and Syzygium rowlandii); Te. Ta-Sagbe (as for other Garcinia spp); Ko. Sagbe; Cr. Bita-kola

19. Gilbertiodendron spp.: Me. Gugui, Gogoi

20. Hymenocardia spp: Me. Fagbanjui (–joi), Nja– fagbanjui; Te. Ka–Gbalkəntha; Ki. Lɔlɔ-kumsa; Ko. Fagbanji; Sh. Gbathan-dɛ

21. Invingia gabonensis: Me. Bɔbɔi; Te. An–gbere; Ko. Gbele, Kpele, Mbei; Lo. Kɛɛga.

22. Manihot exculentus: Me. Tangai

23. Mareya micrantha: Me. nwanwai; Te. An–Gbesen; Ki. Lamba; Ko. Nɔnang na; Kor. Ware–warɛ; Sh. nwanwa-lɛ; Lo nwanwa: Cr. Nɔmba–wan.

24. Millettia spp.: Me. Heilegbamei, Tɔlugbɛlei; Te. Ka–Lin, Ra–Sapo; Ki. Nyanga; Ko. Katindane, Taugbe; Lo. Neigbahma.

25. Musanga cecropioides: Me. Ngovui; Te. An-Fekan; Ki. Peindo; Ko. Wunsonɛ; Kor Wunson; Lo. Ngogho

26. Ochthocosmus africanus: Me. Tɔwanyɛi, Twanyɛi; Te. Ka–Thɔnai; Ki. Tundui–halo; Ko. Tɔwanɛ, Tuata; Kor. Buwulokoloma; Lo. Fɛgurugoongo.

27. Octoknema borealis: Me. Gijii, Gisii, Kɔtu-wuli; Te. Am-Fuk; Ko. Kongbo-kɔne; Kor. Began, Kuramachembɛ

28. Parinari excelsa.: Me. Nda-wei.(-hei); Te. Am-Bis; Ki. Kwalo; Ko. Koa, Kola; kor. Kurɛ Sh. Bal–lɛ; Lo. Ndawa; Cr. Rof-skin-plɔm, Roffin–plɔm

29. Pentaclethra mycrophlla: Me. Fawei, Faa, Fa–wuli; Te. An–Fal; Ki. Fa; Ko. Faa; Kor. Gbangban; Lo. Fakha.

30. Phylanthus diocoideus.: Me. Tijoi, kɔngɔ-lijoi, Ngogo–lijoi; Te Ka–Saka; Ki. Cholondo, Solondo; Ko. Tisoɛ ; Tusuɛ; Kor. Yɛgerɛ; Sh. Nɛnkon–dɛ; Lo. Tihu

31. Piptadeniastrum africanun: Me. Mbɛlɛi, Mbɛlɛi–gulei; Te. Ka-Bari, Ka-kulbin; Ki. Lolo, peiyɛngɔ; Ko. Mɛɛ (as for Newtonia aubrevillei); Kor. Kornorɛ, Melawula

32. Pycnanthus angolensis.: Me. (G)Kpɔyɛi; Te. Ka-Wor; Ki. Yɔma; Ko. (K)Gbɔsɔne; Kor. Gbonson; Lo. Kpɔhɔru

33. Sacoglottis gabonensis: Me. Kpɔ-wuli; Ko. Gbɔkone.

34. Samanea dinklagei: Me. Gongoi, Gungui, sungui, Ngongoi, Ngungui, Saamei; Te. Ka-Sinɔ Ki. Tamatɔmda, Wongo; Ko. Ongone, Wongone; Kor. Sansan (as for Albizia feruginea), Wonge; Sh. Bonda–lɛ (as for Albizia feruginea)

35. Smeathmannia spp: Me. Ndovotie; Te. Ka-Sete; Ki. Walwa, Y-mchokaicho; Ko. Twɔne Kor. Fira-fingɛ (as for Diospyros spp), Korenyankon; Sh. Buwe–lɛ, Bue–lɛ

36. Spondias mombia: Me. Gboji; Te. An–Lɔp; Ki. Lewo; Ko. Kpanginɛ; Sh. Le–lɛ; Lo. Kpaki; Cr. Fiks–plɔm, Hɛl– faiya–pɔm.

37. Sterculia trangacantha: Me. Kobei; Te. Ka-Gbɔfrɔk; Ki. Bɔndɔ; Ko. Fangbandɛ; Kor. Deinkiranafun, Famgbandɛ; Lo. Koba; Cr. Abala-lif

38. Uapaca guineensis.: Me. Kondii; Te. An-Lil; Ki. Kaango; Ko. Suanɛ (as for U. esculenta); Kor. Dombɛ or Dumbɛ, Nerɛ-kɛrɛ; Sh. Tuo–lɛ; Lo. Kondi

39. Vitex micrantha: Me. Fɛvɛi; Ki. Gbema, Lɔlɔ-kumsa

40. Xylopia aethiopica: Me. Hewei; Te. Ma-Pos, Ma–Tel; Ki. Siawo; Ko. Kandi (as for Anisophyllea spp); Sh. Son–dɛ; Lo. Seve; Cr. Siminji, Spais–tik.

Additionally, 'basic data' includes binni, Christmas tree, cotton tree, egusi, okra, robusta coffee, sorghum, wild mushroom, wild oil palm, and yoyavii (vernacular – Mende). One indicator alone is not enough to produce reliable information for the farmer. To decide on an activity, the farmer requires a combination of indicators comprising plant and animal species, soil conditions, and weather conditions.

Data Messages

This is the transformation of 'basic data' into 'data messages' to reach a decision. A successful season for the upland rice farmer is about making the right decision at the appropriate time. In producing the 'data message', the 'basic data' is aggregated into pieces of information. Data message entails messages understandable to those with the relevant knowledge in upland rice farming to decode what they inhered. They are no longer a single entity of 'basic data'. At this stage, the information is seen only as a message, which requires acknowledgement and given meaning by the receiver. These messages are information for the receiver to consolidate, assess, appraise and transform into an understandable message. To do this, the individual must have a well-informed background in indigenous knowledge of traditional upland rice farming.

At this stage, the data are no longer simply items in everyday life. They will show signs, signalling and directing the farmer to grasp the message concerning the farming events and practices. The changes occurring in the species are associated with specific farm events, with the combination of physical environmental changes forming the 'basic information data' that is useable in decision making.

It is vital to note the difference between 'basic data' and 'basic information data'. The latter is the product of the processing of 'data message', in combination with other information, such as the practice in hand and availability of labour at specific times of the farming calendar. It is like the dovetail of what begins with 'basic data', stemming into 'data messages' and then streaming into 'basic information data' geared toward decision making.

One farmer alone cannot understand all the data messages in traditional upland rice farming. Those who lack the requisite indigenous knowledge may regard farm practices as activities to perform at a prescribed time. They rely on knowledgeable farmers to take the lead that they may follow. They burn their farms when they see that other farmers have started burning. They may not realise that the farmers they are trying to follow have taken certain precautions into account before burning their farms at the time that they did, and the conditions may not be the same on their farmland. Their information management is basically on imitating rather than 'know how'. This group of farmers can benefit from credible information management and dissemination agencies in the form of extension services grounded in information management in upland rice farming. This is where the effective recognition and usage of the 'data messages' becomes a significant factor in supporting farmers with rice production.

While serving as extension workers in the SLC/CCD programme, we faced a predicament in 1988, resulting from a prolonged delay in the rainy season. After we distributed the seed loan to the farmers, they did their sowing based on the imminent expectation of the rains, as usual. With the unpredicted delay, there were widespread anxieties across the farming communities and ourselves as extension agents that we were heading for a disaster of total crop failure with the ultimate losses. Our only option, as extension workers, was to monitor the situation while resigned to the fate of Mother Nature.

Most of the extension team had given up until I ran into an elderly experienced farmer who allayed my apprehension concerning where we were heading. He explained that the delay should not be alarming at that stage because the soil will continue to serve as extended storage until the rains start. The only action, he advised, was the additional labour required to scare the birds from eating up the seeds. He put the worries of the other farmers down to their inexperience and lack of knowledge. Taking that message back to the team was a massive relief and immense satisfaction of assurance. It became our extension message to the other farmers. As that farmer anticipated, the rains finally arrived, symbolically washing away all the fears and anxieties about the potential losses. The seeds germinated to the vindication of that single farmer. We got the credit as astute extension workers at the time, but I would hand it back to that farmer by mentioning him, to give an example of how and what we can learn from farmers. That was a perfect example of the tacit nature of indigenous knowledge in upland rice farming and a significant point of learning for myself, and the team that we can rely on indigenous knowledge in managing information on upland rice farming.

Information in use

The user is ultimately the most important recipient of data messages to acquire meaning and value. Before this stage of information usage, it is a mere data message. Information management is a process involving a sequence of thoughts for the individual. For this reason, the working knowledge of the individual is vital. Farmers are the final destination of information processing in traditional farming as well as the processing of new information.

With an understanding of how different categories of farmers use information, professionals can support them in the overall information management system. How older farmers use information differs from the younger farmers based on the differences in knowledge and experiences.

Likewise, the information needs of individual farmers vary. Women in traditional upland rice farming perform specialised tasks and therefore have different needs in information management from the men. This speciality in knowledge is along the gender division of labour. While the women might have accumulated knowledge in cropping patterns due to their role in mixing seeds, broadcasting and weeding the rice crop, the men might have accumulated knowledge and skills in site selection, brushing, fencing and burning. Central to this concept is the understanding that farmers have an available and useable store of knowledge (their working knowledge), organised into a structure held in memory and reference materials, although not in published literature. The store of knowledge is continuously updated and modified by additions, removals and reorganisation in their personal and local information management systems. This knowledge is what they use in making decisions in their farming practices (Rolls et al., 1987, p 1).

The nature of the information and data obtained from indigenous knowledge reported above has shown that it can be inputted into computerised information technology packaged as 'basic data' to generate 'data messages'. The following discussion is on how researchers, experts, extension services, scientists and policymakers might facilitate the process of information management in upland rice farming in Sierra Leone, using farmers' indigenous knowledge and IT systems.

The use of computers and the Internet

Agricultural information Technology (AIT) is broadly applied to every aspect of agriculture in developed countries and has become the most effective means and tool for enhancing productivity using agricultural resources. The use of technology in Agriculture Information Management, as a sub-technology of AIT, directly affects the degree of Agricultural information and efficiency of production and decision-making (Yan-e D, 2011). Farm management information systems (FMIS) have steadily increased in their level of sophistication as they have included new technologies, with internet connectivity being the latest addition. However, few FMIS have used the full capabilities of the internet, and the emerging concept of precision agriculture has little or no support in the current commercially available FMIS. (Raimo Nikkilä, Ilkka Seilonen, Kari Koskinen, 2010).

Information technology comprises computer hardware, software and electronic devices used in information, storage, retrieval, processing and usage. In using computers to manage information obtained from indigenous knowledge, the data collected has to be initially identified as 'basic data', and then transformed into 'data messages' for codifying. Each 'basic data' and 'data message' is given a unique number, e.g. '01' for 'mushrooms' ('basic data') and

'02' for 'mushrooms will sprout' (data message), 03 for 'what it indicates for which specific practice', that is information in use. Following that, the computer screen is formatted to match the data-collecting instrument.

Statistical packages and spreadsheets are used, after the data entry, for statistical analysis, hypothesis and inference drawing purposes. A network of computer operations will link research institutions and extension services involved in fostering and promoting a coordinated information management system in upland rice farming.

Computers are versatile tools that can rapidly analyse large quantities of data to produce information and its management. The most applicable development concerning information management for farmers is the connection that can be made between television sets and distant computers so that the information can be received and displayed. This technology is called Videotext.

The type of Videotext most applicable to farmers is Teletext. In Teletext, the information obtained from traditional indigenous knowledge can be pre-coded and broadcast, though the questions of validation and adaptation may arise. This kind of facility can only be available with the requisite development in the communication network in the country as a whole, with its limitations and drawbacks.

Geographical Transect

Geographical transits are observatory walks to study natural resources, indigenous practices, topography, local technology, soil and vegetation, which may include species related to farming practices. This walk requires experienced farmers willing to share their knowledge and experiences with inexperienced colleagues and development workers. During the transect, researchers can collect plant and animal species identified by farmers in the form of laboratories as reference materials.

A typical transect of upland rice farming is a combination of the social aspect of the local infrastructure and amenities, religious practices, cultural features and behaviours, economic activities, farming techniques and other occupations, like the blacksmith, in so far as they relate to farming.

There are different types of transects, among which two broad categories are the social and land-use transects. To use indigenous knowledge in information management in traditional upland rice farming the 'Land-use' transect is a valuable tool. It focuses on environmental and local agricultural features, such as cropping and cultivation practices, forest management, ranges, barren lands and erosion phenomena, and natural resources including streams, bodies of water, soil types and natural vegetation. The nature of transects in the case of upland rice farming should take the form of observational walks during which special attention is on the indigenous farming practices, related resources and environmental factors.

A transect can be in a meandering way that follows the features of common interest to the observers. The walk can be in a straight line cutting the terrain in a specific way, such as a compass direction. Transect walks of this kind help to verify the information provided on maps afterwards, both through direct observations and in discussion groups. Ideally, the walk should be in small groups to maximise the opportunity for open participation and interactions.

The issue is that the wealth of knowledge and information in upland rice farming has remained underutilised in the country. Attempts to increase agricultural productivity through improved technology have focused primarily on relatively well-endowed areas of physical resources, infrastructure and a narrow range of staple cereals. While this so-called Green Revolution approach has been very successful in output growth, the effects on equity have been more diffuse, depending on the nature of poverty in a given area. Other factors, e.g. institutional inadequacy, population growth and labour displacing mechanisation have also influenced equity issues.

The awareness of the consequences of the modern varieties has led to the search for new approaches in technology development and land use planning that would include disadvantaged groups. The argument is that the integration of land evaluation and farming systems analysis can substantially improve current practices in land use planning, as an aid for sustainable land use and rural development.

In recent years, sustainability has become a major concept to describe the successful management of resources for agriculture to satisfy changing human needs while maintaining or improving the quality of the environment and conserving natural resources (TAC, 1988). Although methods to assess sustainability are still in their development stages, there is little doubt that the intensification of land use at low external input levels is hardly sustainable.

Today one is likely to witness changing demands on land use, increased needs to deploy efforts in marginal areas and growing concerns about environmental issues. Under these conditions, designing sustainable land use systems capable of meeting qualitatively and quantitatively expanding needs of the population in developing countries presents an enormous challenge to all those concerned—policymakers, planners, scientists and, last but not least, the population itself.

What is needed is a clear assessment of the potential of the land and the existing farming systems like upland rice farming, as well as the identification of ways to attain these potentials to develop adequate and sustainable land use plans (Louise O. Fresco Herman G.J. Huizing Hermen Van Keulen Henk A. Luning Robert, Schipper A., 1999).

For a sustainable land use plan nowadays, the land use planning (LUP) approach requires more and more data integration, multi-disciplinary and complex analysis, and faster or more precise information for the participants in the LUP approaches.

Geographic Information System (GIS), which has a strong capacity for data integration for analysis and visualization, becomes the tool for supporting LUP approaches (N.H. Trung, L.Q. Tri, Van Mensvoort M.E.F. and Bregt A.K., 2006).

Primary Resource Mapping

Agriculture describes routine activities related to weather change; water is a centre point of the components, whether used directly for agricultural or non-agricultural purposes (Adikant Pradhan, S.K. Patil, T. Chandrakar, S.K. Nag and S.C. Mukherjee, 2019). Agriculture takes advantage of the nutrients in the soil and the moisture available to the crop. Water is the key. When crops aren't getting enough water, farmers have to find ways to bring water to the crops. Humans have learned how to change the environment to boost crop production. We have also acquired the skills to produce more crops with less land. However, there remain many issues that threaten agriculture sustainability the world over. For example, population increase, unprecedented climate changes, and water impact on farming.

For farmers to rise to the challenges of the impact of moisture stress and the management of their farming practices, they must keep abreast with the necessary 'information management' on the causal effects of climate change and the resulting environmental changes (GIS Geography, October 29, 2021).

Primary resource mapping provides an overview of the local farming situation. Primary Resource Mapping presents information on indigenous knowledge in natural resource management, including land, water, trees, soil types, cropping patterns, productivity, watershed, degraded land, and agro-forestry. Primary Resource Mapping can be a tool for managing forest and bush fallow. Repeated participatory mapping, periodically, may help to monitor and evaluate changes in the land management system and take appropriate actions to amend any unfavourable conditions akin to deforestation and land degradation before they get out of control. It usually starts with collective discussions among groups and then proceeds to draw maps of their perceptions about the geographical distribution of the local environmental and social resources. This process will help to identify the natural resources, for example, the bush/forest fertility for upland rice, vis-à-vis the existing land tenure system.

Seasonality Diagrams

Seasonality is a characteristic of a time series in which the data experiences regular and predictable changes that recur every calendar year. Any predictable fluctuation or pattern that recurs or repeats over one year is said to be seasonal (Will Kenton, 2020). Seasonality diagrams can generate indigenous knowledge in information management on specific aspects such as the seasonal pattern of rainfall, timeliness of the different farm events and operations, information sources and management and indigenous credit institutions. Farmers who possess a wealth of indigenous knowledge and are willing to share them with less knowledgeable and inexperienced farmers should be encouraged to get involved in the exercises. The team of farmers must have shared tasks. The outside observers must listen, learn and take down important notes. Any views and opinions on which the farmers differ for further discussion and verification are noted for discussion. The reports will represent the indigenous knowledge in that particular location.

The use of video recordings and the collection of species can facilitate the production of reference materials. The information recorded on the indigenous knowledge from such exercises can then be transformed by codification (given unique codes) from 'basic data' to 'data messages' and 'information in use' to be made available for computer processing in information management.

Documentation centres/Rural libraries

Documentation is a viable way of capturing and storing information for its management. Information on indigenous knowledge can be collected through formal interviews, administering questionnaires, farmers' workshops and informally as in rural appraisals. The most important aspect is the presentation in an accessible and easily readable form for the farmers and target population. That kind of document can be used in the pedagogue for rural farmers through regular farmers' forums at the village community levels. It will serve as the opportunity to validate, update and transform indigenous knowledge by including the farmers themselves. This exercise involves both the rural people and development workers. The results produced are documented for reference purposes. With the professional guidance, there is the need to back up farmers' interpretations with scientific experimentations and interpretations. From the farmers and professional interactions, the essence of Participatory Rural Appraisal will emerge, wherein indigenous knowledge will provide information for policy formulation.

It will be necessary to have publications from indigenous knowledge on upland rice farming held at centres in rural areas where they can be accessible to the farmers as users. The centres should be managed by people trained in handling and managing those facilities, who know how to assess the information held there and be able to provide an interface to the users. In Ghana, for example, farmers are given the relevant information they need for the expected high quality and quantity of food, cash crops and animal production required to meet the nutritional demands of the growing Ghanaian population. In this vein, librarians and information workers should actively participate in disseminating agricultural information to farmers using audio-visual materials, tools and Information Communication Technologies. By providing agricultural information for farmers improvements in practices for high yields can be achieved.

Librarians should play an active part in making useful agricultural information readily available. Agricultural librarians, researchers and extension officers can get information from the internet and various databases on agriculture and make the same available to farmers in the manner and languages they can understand to ensure faster agricultural development (Lamptey R B, Sambo I A, Hassan A, 2017).

A great deal of translation is required so that the reference materials can be available in the local languages of the people in the region. Adult literacy classes will be necessary for raising the literacy of the farmers in their native languages to use the reference materials.

Botanical Gardens

A wide range of plant species has been identified in this book as reported by the upland rice farmers relating to their upland rice farming. Notwithstanding, the majority of young and inexperienced farmers in the country cannot identify most of the species. With the knowledge of experienced farmers, the plant and animal species can be collected, with the plants in into botanical gardens for identification and educational purposes, allowing laboratory studies by botanists and plant breeders on whether their relationship with the farming system goes beyond what the farmers have established from their personal and collective observations and experimentations. It can serve as valuable information for farmers, scholars, researchers and extension workers in joint information management programmes.

Human activities have caused adverse impacts on the earth's ecosystems, creating environmental problems (Sathaye et al. 2007). It has happened at such unprecedented levels that we have ushered in a new geologic period called the Anthropocene (Zalasiewicz et al. 2010).

According to reports, more than 80% of the earth's surface has been altered by human activities, with two-thirds of major marine fisheries overexploited (or depleted), and the global biodiversity loss in the face of a changing climate has led to expected and unexpected threats to the current and future populations (Estes et al. 2011; FAO 2013; Folke et al. 2004).

Given the fact that human activities are at the centre of environmental issues, sustainable development ultimately depends on changing human behaviour. However, promoting public engagement and individual actions remains a challenge for governments and institutions worldwide (Gifford 2011; Weber and Johnson 2012; Whitmarsh, Lorenzoni, and O'Neill 2012).

There is an exciting opportunity for changemakers to explore innovative ways to promote responsible consumption and resource management and to implement sustainable strategies and practices across private and public life (Lubchenco 1998; Raskin et al. 2002).

Psychologists, anthropologists, and ecologists have long maintained that human connection with nature is a crucial determinant of people's worldview and behaviour (Bateson 1979; Rees 2002; Walker et al. 2004). In a culture where environmental problems have resulted from a growing disconnection from the natural world, botanical gardens are uniquely situated to contribute to sustainability, education and global conservation while fulfilling their horticultural goals (Suzuki and McConnell 2007).

The majority of botanical gardens around the world already promote research, plant conservation, and public education through their courses, tours, and events (Dodd and Jones 2010). Interest in education for sustainable development has grown with these gardens working to broaden audiences and diversify programs (Williams et al. 2015). With over 3300 botanical institutions and Public Gardens around the world receiving over 240 million visitors per year (Botanical Gardens Conservation International 2018), there is a tremendous, untapped opportunity for gardens to reconnect communities with the natural world, illustrate the web of connections and motivate individual attitude and action toward a more sustainable future.

Publications

Publications of traditional indigenous knowledge on upland rice farming in the form of books, manuals, leaflets, journals and magazines, when written in the local languages and updated periodically, can be helpful in information management at the farm level. In the United Kingdom and other parts of the world, where information is a valuable productive resource in farming, sources of information are sought after by farmers. Similar facilities (when produced) using indigenous knowledge can increase the chances of using indigenous knowledge in information management. They can provide literary materials for extension courses in the country.

Audio-visual materials, Documentaries and Broadcast

The use of audio-visual material is not new in extension. However, most of the information formerly used was on external scientific knowledge in agriculture. With advanced information technology, audio-visual materials are now available using the information on indigenous knowledge in participatory rural appraisals in many parts of the world. Similar materials can be produced using the information on indigenous knowledge on upland rice farming, presented in songs or stories composed by singers, talented farmers and professionals. The compositions are useful to convey extension messages to optimise the use of traditional indigenous knowledge. These materials can also be of use in designing educational training programmes for farmers and students following agriculture extension courses in the universities.

The use of mass media has led to an increase in the knowledge level and output of the educational system in recent decades. It seems the main reason for the popularity of television lies in its simplicity for the audiences. Since people intend to choose the easiest way of learning, the simplest of conveying information messages can be via television educational programs (Buren, 2000).

Ekoja (2003) stated that the information sources on the different agricultural topics for the farmers are radio and television, propagation publications, daily farm newspapers, agriculture exhibitions, practical education, and consultation services, respectively.

Arokoyo (2003) showed that videos, radio, and television are the primary sources of information for the farmers in Nigeria. Among the items in mass media regarding informal education, radio and television have a specific situational location in farming systems. Due to its wide usage, the media is among the best educational and cultural instruments.

The success of agricultural development programmes in developing countries largely depends on the nature and extent of the use of mass media in mobilising people for their development goals. Radio and television could be the most effective media for diffusing scientific knowledge to the masses. In countries where literacy in rural areas is low, the choice of communication media is of vital importance. Under those circumstances, television and radio are significant, as they transfer modern agricultural technology to literate and illiterate farmers alike, even in interior areas, within a short time (Nazari and Hasbullah, 2008). Television is acknowledged as the most important medium for communicating with the rural populations of developing countries (FAO, 2001).

Documentaries and broadcasts can be in the form of films, television programmes, or radio broadcasts, which provides factual, validated information on indigenous knowledge on traditional upland rice farming. Documentaries can be particularly useful in transect walks. A documentary backed up by documentation can produce an indigenous 'information bank'. 'Information banks' are crucial in indigenous knowledge systems because most of the knowledge is in the heads of the old farmers. As they die, their knowledge is lost. This body of knowledge could be captured and stored for usage and posterity via documentation and broadcast services.

Telephone Information Services

These services provide the means of disseminating pre-coded information. They have the advantage of speed, making information readily available to a broad spectrum of farming communities in response to changing situations, for example, pricing and market information, weather forecasts, and pest and disease control measures.

Information derived from indigenous knowledge on traditional upland rice farming can be pre-coded for similar services and its wider dissemination to the farming communities in the country. It could be advising farmers on what they should be looking out for in their environment, for example, to assist with the timeliness of their decisions on their farming practices.

Horizontal Extension

'Horizontal Extension' is the practice of transferring information from successful and experienced farmers to inexperienced farmers. A well-coordinated approach by researchers and extension workers can facilitate the use of indigenous knowledge in information management by identifying the less experienced farmers and linking them with experienced ones. Information sharing is already taking place in the farming communities among the farmers. The aim should be to facilitate, coordinate, and promote the existing channels.

Agricultural Field Day

Information management in indigenous knowledge on upland rice farming mentioned above can form the theme of regional Agricultural Field Days around the country, where farmers, professionals, researchers, and students following agricultural extension courses can learn from each other in a relaxed and sociable atmosphere. An Agricultural Field Day is a way of Agricultural extension teaching and learning from the display of 'method and result demonstrations' and 'farmers' competitions with incentives and rewards for excellence, all in the spirit and atmosphere of socialisation, with cultural performances and displays, music and dancing.

Geographical Information System (GIS)

The key objective of this chapter is to present methods and tools for managing information derived from indigenous knowledge and other data sources on traditional upland rice farming in Sierra Leone. A Geographic Information System (GIS) is a tool that creates visual representations of data and performs spatial analyses to assist users in making informed decisions. GIS is a technology that combines hardware, software, and data. The data can represent almost anything imaginable so long as it has a geographic component. Hardware can be anything from desktop computers or laptops to satellites, drones, and handheld Global Positioning System (GPS) units.

A key feature of GIS is that it is location-specific, which bears similarity to indigenous knowledge in upland rice farming in terms of location specificity to the farming community and region (Dornich K, Hammonds T, 2017).

The real power of GIS lies in its ability to analyse multiple layers of data and variables. GIS can transform and combine large amounts of data into a data set. It does this by representing data about real-world phenomena as points, lines and polygons into homogenous formats stored as individual layers of databases.

GIS has the capacity of an effective and efficient means of collecting, storing, manipulating, analysing and disseminating information data obtained from different sources. This capacity allows GIS to incorporate all of the information gathered from the other methods of information management mentioned above into a robust, all-encompassing, integrated information management system in upland rice farming, therein enhancing the preservation of indigenous knowledge on traditional farming systems.

GIS has thousands of applications, and it continues to make innovations, that benefit our everyday lives. GIS can be used to analyse soil data combined with historical farming practices to determine the best crops to plant in a specific location, where on the farmland they should go, and how to maintain soil nutrition levels to best benefit the plants (Tripathi N, Shefali and Bhattarya, 2017).

The indisputable recognition is that droughts, floods, swarms of insects and poor farming techniques have plagued the agricultural community for centuries. There have been improvements to ensure the safety of crops worldwide through crop protection measures, yet these constraints and many more continue to devastate the affected individuals and their communities. With the use of GIS, more complex spatial analyses for agriculture can compare variables like soil type; soil density and degradation; wind direction; the amount of rainfall; slope, and topography; to assist with crop management, site suitability, and drainage planning, as well as risk prevention from flood, drought, erosion, and plant disease. GIS can help farmers adapt to these different variables, monitor the health of individual crops, and estimate yields to maximise their production (Dornich K, Hammonds T, 2017).

GIS is instrumental in the efforts to end global hunger by using land use and primary food crop statistics in combination with data collected by satellites and mobile devices to identify areas in need and the underlying causes of food insecurity. Satellites, drones, and manned aircraft are used for remote sensing. Remote sensing involves gathering information about the earth's surface by scanning it from high altitudes. The Landsat 8 is an observation satellite that orbits the earth every 16 days as a joint effort of the United States Geographical Survey (USGS) and the National Aeronautics and Space Administration (NASA). It captures nine bands of the visible light spectrum, capable of calculating factors like plant diseases, nutrient deficiencies, insect infestations, crop moisture excesses and shortages (Dornich K, Hammonds T, 2017).

A significant source of data for GIS is remote sensing. Campbell and Wynne 2011, define remote sensing as the practice of deriving information about the earth's land and water surfaces using images acquired by aircraft-based and satellite-based sensor technologies from an overhead perspective, using electromagnetic radiation in one or more regions of the electromagnetic spectrum, reflected or emitted from the earth's surface. Depending on the surface temperature, the intensity of the wavelengths emitted by different types of vegetation and the effects of various human activities, our natural landscapes tend to differ from one location to another.

The implication for crop production is that what may be the best fit for one location may not be the same for another. Remote sensing can capture thermal infrared radiation (TIR), which is generally outside the range of human vision. The recorded data are converted into visible digital imagery applicable to general objectives like managing water for irrigation, detecting plant disease, and preventive measures against droughts, floods, and soil erosion (Dornich K, Hammonds T, 2017).

GIS has become an integral part of automated field operations, also referred to as Precision Agriculture or Satellite Farming. With the rapid developments in Global Positioning Systems (GPS), unmanned aerial vehicles (UAV), and robotics technologies, many farm tasks are becoming computerised. In developed countries, farmers have improved their decision-making capabilities for planning their cultivation to maximise yields by using data collected from remote sensors and sensors mounted directly on farm machinery.

Previous crop yields, terrain specifics, organic matter content, soil pH (the measure of the acidity and basicity of the soil), soil moisture, and the nutrient levels of the soil, aid in proper preparation for precision farming. GIS is incredibly helpful in mapping and projecting current and future fluctuations in factors like precipitation, temperature, crop output, and many more that would go undetected as vital information goes unnoticed and is missed altogether (Elizabeth Borneman, 2014).

Variable Rate Technology (VRT) is the component of precision agriculture which allows the direct use of data. VRT joins farm machinery, control systems, and equipment to apply precise amounts of growing inputs at the exact time and location. Precision Farming combined with VRT has both economic and environmental advantages. It is applicable in sowing seeds, tweaking nutrients, applying fertilizer, and using pesticides only where and when needed. This can have substantial cost savings for the farmer and boost revenues. Negative environmental impacts from the over-application of chemicals are alleviated, coupled with the potential for eliminating the unnecessary use of certain chemicals based on data analysis (Dornich K, Hammonds T, 2017).

The use of precision farming in upland rice farming can fill the gaps in the farmers' indigenous knowledge and information management to promote the development of effective, efficient and economic upland rice farming practices in Sierra Leone. Geographic Information System provides a framework for documenting and storing indigenous knowledge meaningfully. Participation by the local community in development initiatives is critical for achieving sound natural resource management to utilize the full potential of Indigenous Knowledge Systems and ensure sustainability.

We have learned from experience that development efforts that ignore indigenous knowledge, local systems of knowledge, and local environmental information generally fail to achieve their desired objectives. Indigenous Knowledge Systems are becoming extinct because of the rapidly changing natural and social environments. The integration of indigenous knowledge with Geographic Information Systems helps to promote participatory natural resource management, thus allowing the local community to participate in development programmes and decision-making both as contributors and users of knowledge (Tripathi N, Shefali and Bhattarya, 2017).

Agricultural Geographic Information Systems (AGIS) maps topography and crop health and helps to solve the economic issues in municipalities and urban centres that stem from rural farming practices. By mapping geographic and geologic features of current and potential farmland, scientists and farmers can work together to create more effective and efficient farming techniques in indigenous farming practices. This approach will increase food production in parts of the world struggling to produce enough for the local people (Borneman E, 2014).

As resource managers search for strategies to meet the challenges posed by intense competition for scarce local resources, the implementation of Community-based GIS applications has become widespread. In an era where Participatory Geographical Information Systems (PGIS) applications have become vital in managing local resources, there is an urgent need to examine the usage of GIS in the management of information in indigenous farming systems (Kyem P.A.K, Saku J. C, 2017).

By using AGIS, scientific knowledge of the geology and geography of a specific place can be related by a unique identifier in a GIS environment as long as there is a spatial component to it. AGIS can be used to obtain information on indigenous knowledge in upland rice farming in Sierra Leone for specific areas to overcome the problem of losing valuable knowledge when the farmer passes away.

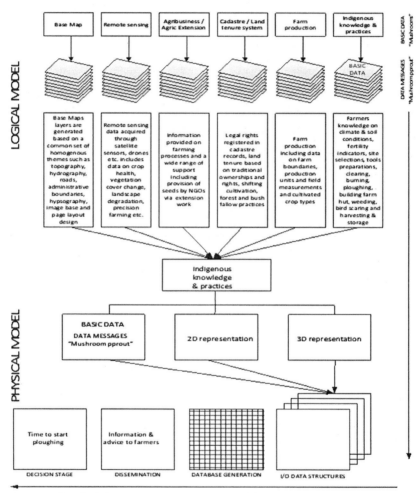

Plate 14: GIS Data Management Model – E Macauley & J Patewa (2022)

Summary

The ongoing adaptation of indigenous knowledge to particular situations, environments and cultural niches has significant value for the livelihood of the farm family and the farming community in Sierra Leone. However, it must not go without acknowledgement that indigenous knowledge has limitations with the rapidly emerging socio-economic pressures. It will be erroneous, therefore, to claim that every item of indigenous knowledge on traditional upland rice farming conceals grains of scientific truth (Chambers, 1993). As such, the proclamation of indigenous knowledge in upland rice farming as accomplished without the necessary validation by farmers and professionals can be inappropriate and misleading since some mythical credence can lead to irrational thinking and behaviour.

Not every farmer understands the rationale behind the indigenous knowledge used in every aspect of their farm practices. When asked why this is so, one elderly farmer in one of our village group discussions in the Pujehum district told me that it was not respectful, in their times, for people to question the ideas of elders. Hence they only took on board what they observed as gospel truth without seeking or querying the reasoning. Besides, the practices worked and achieved the desired outcomes, and the need for questioning did not arise or cross the mind.

Swift (1979), Biggs and Clay (1980) identified the following as some of the limitations in the use of indigenous knowledge in information management; that indigenous knowledge and innovative capacity are not distributed evenly within and across the communities; the abilities of individual farmers to generate indigenous knowledge and derive, implement and transfer information from it vary greatly; the transfer and use of information, are sometimes cumbersome where it is held in the heads of farmers and has to be passed on orally; the scope for improvement from 'pure' indigenous knowledge is limited to what can be done with the local pool of techniques, materials and genetic resources; the affiliations to social groups and economic stratification affect the type and extent to which individuals can access and possess indigenous knowledge; indigenous knowledge is called into question when farmers face external interventions that fail to embrace their knowledge, likewise the adverse effects of environmental crisis, war and civil unrest as was in the case of the many years of rebel incursions on the farming communities in Sierra Leone.

Recognising its limitations, merits, and values will help to take a balanced view of the importance of indigenous knowledge alongside farmers' potential for innovations in any programme geared towards the sustainability of traditional practices in upland rice farming in Sierra Leone.

Formal science tends to insulate itself from large areas of life, such as the dimensions of upland rice farming, by disregarding everything which does not fit neatly with its categories of thoughts and universality (Chambers 1993). It has to be understood that any scientific intervention into traditional indigenous knowledge on upland rice farming should be cognisant of the socio-cultural context in which it exists. The intervention must clarify whether it aims to legitimise indigenous knowledge solely in the eyes of the scientific community or whether to strengthen and maintain the wholeness of its cultural identity and integrity (Chambers, 1993).

Juma (1987) argues that local farmers might go with the perception that their indigenous knowledge is delegitimised and trivialised if it is isolated from its cultural context and forced into the context of western epistemology. Thrupp (1987) presented a similar argument that merely collecting what is considered relevant and logical scientific items from indigenous knowledge into tailor-made 'scientific packages' while discarding what is regarded as scientifically irrelevant and irrational will tend to devalue the concept as outdated, primitive and archaic.

Upland rice farming based on indigenous knowledge has remained the only reliable source of sustaining the livelihoods of the vast majority of the rural population in Sierra Leone. This calls for a significant shift in interest and thinking in any drive to increase rice production in the country. Recognising the indigenous knowledge of the farmers has to be the starting point, at least, in seeking the answer to the question of; how can we support our farmers to help themselves with the cumulative effect of increasing food production in the country.

Managing information derived from indigenous knowledge in decision-making in upland rice farming is nothing new. This book and other published literature reveal that upland rice farmers in Sierra Leone have been doing this within their capacity from time immemorial. What is lacking is the deserving acknowledgement of the importance of the usage of indigenous knowledge by the vast majority of professionals, academics, and practitioners in the country. Most professionals claim to be the experts with the technical know-how, advice and solutions to offer to the farmers without the realisation that, on the contrary, they need to learn about how the farmers use their knowledge to manage the information on their farming practices.

Chapter seven covers a range of possible methods to assist upland rice farmers and practitioners in information management using information derived from indigenous knowledge. Firstly, to achieve these levels of information management, there has to be a political will to provide the basic infrastructure for an effective communication network in the country. Secondly, there should be the necessary facilities and devices to enhance the appropriate networks to manage information to benefit the farming communities.

Essentially the success of information management in other farming systems and communities is only possible because of the existence, and availability of efficient communication networks, with easier access to information technologies and the affordability of the necessary gadgets in those countries.

Biggelaar (1991) encapsulates the overarching tenet of this book with the salient point that agricultural development strategies in the indigenous communities, to date, are chiefly based on western technological solutions, with mixed success rates.

Farming Systems Research (FSR), was advanced to increase the use of indigenous knowledge on farming to make new technologies more adaptable and appropriate to local farming conditions. While FSR has enabled researchers to focus on people and their knowledge, by increasing people's participation in problem identification and new technology validation, in practice, FSR continues to be a top-down approach: technologies continue to be developed (in most cases) in the exogenous, western knowledge system.

In his paper, Biggelaar adapted a model from Martin Bell (1979), based on cooperation and collaboration between the exogenous and indigenous knowledge systems leading to a synthesis of the two. The underlying principle of Bell's model is that the ultimate solution for rural development is not the mere dumping of more scientists upon rural people (of whatever discipline), to make exogenously, generated technologies more adaptable in line with people's problems. A more productive approach would involve strengthening, empowering, and embracing the indigenous capacities for identifying limitations and developing solutions for these problems.

It is empowering to acknowledge indigenous knowledge (however difficult it may be politically) so that it has equal footing with "western knowledge". It may well be the most significant step in a strategy of enabling farmers in developing countries to alleviate their poverty. In the case of upland rice farming in Sierra Leone, the potential springboard is recognising the importance of using their indigenous knowledge in information management in their farming practices to increase their productivity.

Conclusion and Recommendations

Increasing food production, particularly rice production, is crucial to the prospect of agricultural development in Sierra Leone. Upland rice farming is the primary source of food production in the country. In the case of upland rice farmers, farming is a way of life rather than simply an occupation or a set of activities. It is an integral part of their traditional cultures involving their religion, kingship and the fabric of their rural community life.

The ecological and cultural systems in the rural communities of Sierra Leone nowadays are, almost in every aspect, challenged and modified by the pressures in modern times to produce for the market-driven economy and for people to adapt to modern lifestyles. The extent to which upland rice farmers have been able to cope with these pressures has largely been dependent on their ingenuity and the use of their indigenous knowledge.

We are in an era of unprecedented global challenges, with the effects of global warming contributing to adverse climatic and weather conditions at the national, regional, and local levels. Farming practices around the world are, by and large, controlled by local climatic conditions.

Upland rice farmers heavily rely on the prevailing weather conditions at any point in the farming calendar. Farmers often face the dilemma of what to do in the face of unprecedented drastic changes in climatic and weather conditions, which can have devastating effects and disruptions to their farm activities. Upland rice farmers up and down the country need to be prepared to cope with the challenges of global warming. Their indigenous knowledge of forecasting their weather conditions may not always be enough for them to make the right decisions. A poorly burned farm is a glaring example of the consequences of incorrect judgments on the ensuing weather, either due to the unavailability of information, lack of knowledge, or poor information management. The farmer inevitably has to perform piecemeal burning, which requires extra labour and is time-consuming. This eventually causes delays in the following farming

117

activities. A poorly burned farm is said to lack the level of potash, which acts as the key to the base-exchange capacity of the soil for the rice crop.

Experiences in other parts of the world, like the United Kingdom, have shown that producing information for farming is a costly exercise. Nevertheless, farmers in these countries would prefer to pay for information that has some form of insurance than the information given to them free of charge, especially when it does not come from a reliable source.

Upland rice farmers do not record information on their knowledge in writing or audio recording. Their knowledge and information systems are in physical objects, including the natural occurrences they observe in their environmental studies and phenomena like changes in the lunar system. The reference materials used for information management comprise changes in plant species and changes in the behaviours of animals and avian species in their environs resulting from the changing weather and climatic conditions. By referring to specific changes in the species, farmers produce information data that enables them to forecast the weather conditions in making decisions on their farming practices.

Upland rice farmers in Sierra Leone are struggling to meet their subsistent needs more than ever in the history of the farming system. This could be attributed to a range of limiting factors, including population pressure with the increasing demand on the available fallow farmland, demographic, and socioeconomic factors. Added to this is the loss of indigenous knowledge as the experienced and knowledgeable farmers die without any documentation of their knowledge.

Intervention by professionals to assist upland rice farmers in Sierra Leone with their information management is necessary, with support for the procurement of inputs to address the challenges they face in their food production.

Upland rice farmers in Sierra Leone always rely on their indigenous knowledge in managing information in their farm practices. This book has shown that we can obtain information from indigenous knowledge for documentation and transformation into usable forms as reference materials for studies, farm practices and further research. Upland rice farmers always take their time to assess new information using their indigenous knowledge. Even though they obtain their information from the environment, their main aim is to reduce risks in decision-making at the farm level. It is because they invest their day-to-day lives in farming. Any failure can be costly, devastating and often burdensome.

From the discussions with farmers on their information management, there is hardly any universal consensus on all the knowledge on upland rice farming within and across the farming communities. Rather than that, one is more likely to find individual differences of opinion among farmers on indigenous knowledge within the same community.

It is also worth mentioning that there can be noticeable variations in the vernacular pronunciation of the different plant and animal species used as reference materials due to differences in dialects, accentuation and emphasis, even among the same tribes in the various regions of the country. This can cause confusion for professionals and researchers on whether they are referring to the same objects. To avoid confusion farmers should be encouraged to collect the species for identification and discussion at the village community and regional levels, in farmers' workshops and whenever possible on agricultural field days. The role of professionals should be to explore, with the farmers, the possibilities of the applications of farmers' information management at the national level.

To facilitate the process of using indigenous knowledge in information management in Sierra Leone there should be mutual exchanges and interactions between all the existing systems and components, including the farming communities, the extension services and researchers, which are often fragmented. These components need to be unified into a national information management system.

The national information system should strive for synergy by reducing the differentiation and fragmentations between traditional indigenous knowledge and modern scientific agricultural knowledge. Farmers' discussion groups, training workshops and seminars, and agricultural shows are some strategies for integrating Agricultural knowledge and information systems.

Focusing on the rural household as a primary source of information for farmers is a strategic move toward using indigenous knowledge in information management. The revival of the cultural pedagogy in the rural communities by professionals and change agents will benefit young farmers and the future of the farming communities.

The challenge facing rural development workers and agricultural extension services in Sierra Leone today is the odious task of mobilising local resources, including information on promoting low external input agriculture in the face of the increasing cost of importing external inputs. The management of information derived from indigenous knowledge as a viable factor of production is an effective way of meeting this challenge.

Information management between systems primarily takes place at their interfaces. Linkage mechanisms connect information systems at their interface. To facilitate strong linkages there must be cohesion with the consensus in ideology and an effective communication network between all the components for efficient information management. It is a fact that the research and agricultural extension linkage in Sierra Leone is not strong.

Linkages between research, extension services and farmers involve linkage mechanisms. Linkage mechanisms bridge the gaps between the different components serving as the transmitters and conveyors of information management at the interfaces. Linkage mechanisms can be informal collaboration in field trials, coordinating committees with membership drawn from all the components to be operational at regional and national levels, participatory groups of extension workers in on-farm trials conducted by researchers, and involving researchers in rural development projects as social workers. For these mechanisms to be effective, farmers, extension workers, and researchers need to recognise their interdependence, roles and responsibilities with an understanding of each other's goals and objectives.

The key to success in any intervention is the understanding of the prevailing conditions and circumstances. It helps to anticipate what may go wrong and try and avoid them to prevent the situation from worsening. Similarly, it could apply to an intervention in a farming system such as upland rice farming, which has remained virtually unchanged in terms of external interference since its introduction in the country over centuries.

Information management in upland rice farming is effective when recognising the inherent limitations and avoiding the downside of human and technical errors. The prevention of information mismanagement, which could be potentially costly for the farmers, can be done by anticipating undesirable events through collaborative networking involving all the actors, stakeholders, and agencies within the overall information management system for agricultural development in the country.

Individually, farmers have limitations due to the lack of appropriate means for communicating messages from their indigenous knowledge.

Fortunately, information technology can serve as a production and transmission system. It is, therefore, important that an improvement is made in the communication systems in the country to make it possible to fully utilise the available facilities in information technology to manage information generated from indigenous knowledge.

Farmers are individuals with different decision-making strategies. Therefore, their demands for information will ultimately vary. The relationship between the demand and supply of information in upland rice farming is, generally localised at the farmstead, among the rural households, and social contacts in the farming communities. There should be research on the demand and supply of information in traditional upland rice farming to serve as a guide in getting information to the right users according to their needs. It will help to reveal how far indigenous knowledge has met the individual and collective demands of the farmers and who the informants are in the rural communities for specific studies on upland rice farming. What is required is a system of managing information obtained from indigenous knowledge that is easily accessible to all potential users.

It is of great significance to recognise that unlike the colonial government's stance on the method of land clearing as the cause of deforestation, basically on the grounds of economic interest, there is a suggestive approach that integrating agroforestry and forest restoration into upland rice farming could hold the answer to the current concerns over the environmental challenges.

Agroforestry contributes to addressing the problems the world is facing today. From an environmental standpoint, it helps to reduce agriculture's contribution and vulnerability to climate change while also improving the quality and availability of water, among other services (FAO, 2015). A farming technique incorporating the cultivation and conservation of trees among crops or pastureland for more productive and sustainable land use provides immense benefits for forest restoration.

The Food and Agricultural Organisation (FAO) defines agroforestry as a collective name for land-use systems where woody perennials (trees, shrubs, palms, bamboo, and the sort) are deliberately grown on the same land-management units as crops and animals, in some form of spatial arrangement or temporal sequence.

Agroforestry can also be defined as a dynamic, ecologically based, natural resource management system that, through the integration of trees on farms and in the agricultural landscape, diversifies and sustains production for increased social, economic and environmental benefits for land users at all levels.

Agroforestry is crucial to smallholder farmers and other rural people, in particular, because it can enhance their food supply, income and health. Agroforestry systems are multifunctional systems that can provide a wide range of economic, sociocultural, and environmental benefits.

In promoting economic wellbeing, agroforestry can increase and diversify farmers' incomes with access to more nutritious food. In terms of social benefits, agroforestry can empower women, validate indigenous knowledge and improve rural livelihoods (FAO, 2015). In upland rice farming, agroforestry provides practical solutions to local and global environmental problems through agrisilviculture. Agrisilviculture is the combination of crops and trees in the same season.

Much of the work in forest restoration programmes focus on bringing back natural processes that contribute to the forest's productivity and how surface water interacts with the soil, streams, plants, wildlife and the ecosystem. The core elements of forest restoration involve planting trees, improving soil conditions, protecting wildlife corridors and ecology, managing land sustainably and working with governments to promote practices like agroforestry. Soils need microbes and bugs such as centipedes, beetles, and worms to thrive. The health of the restored forest can be radically changed and supported by adding organic matter to the soil (FAO, 2015).

Successful forest restoration programmes must address the needs of small-scale farmers whose access to resources profoundly affects forests. The right approach is to consider the human demands on the forest. Providing people with sustainable access to the natural resources they depend on will create a strategy for repairing natural forest processes. The landscape can support people's needs while taking the pressure off forests that can benefit most from restoration (FAO 2015).

In recognition of the need for forest restoration, upland rice farmers are not negligent, as can be proven in the practice of fallow despite the different approaches and objectives. However, they tend to rely wholly on nature to take its course in their fallow systems. Integrating agroforestry and forest restoration practices into upland rice farming will accelerate and promote the fallow systems. Forest restoration programmes should encourage the local communities to plant seedlings and grow their native trees (FAO, 2015). With the documentation of native species, tree planting can be selective to promote the preponderance of the favourable species.

Geographical Information System (GIS) is the surest way of information management for integrating agroforestry and forest restoration practices in upland rice farming to boost fallow and annihilate adverse environmental effects.

It has been shown in this book that there is a gender division of tasks in upland rice farming. The performances of these tasks are also closely associated with specialised indigenous knowledge along the lines of the gender division of labour. For example, brushing is one of the tasks for men, whereas mixing and the broadcast of seeds during sowing are tasks for women. This creates the necessity for identifying the gender implication when using indigenous knowledge in information management in upland rice farming.

The list of plants, animals, and environmental indicators comprising the 'basic data' and 'data messages' is not exhaustive of what we can derive from indigenous knowledge on upland rice farming. This book is the tip of the iceberg on information management in upland rice farming.

The use of indigenous knowledge in information management should be extended to the different crop farming systems around the country, aiming to make them more open to external interests and academic research for improvements on their usage for increasing productivity and maintaining sustainability.

Finally, it is important to note that the vast majority of the farmers in the country depend upon their indigenous knowledge, which has served them over time, for their farming practices and remains the sole means of meeting their needs for information in their food production. To ignore the acknowledgement of its usefulness or to continue to treat indigenous knowledge on upland rice farming with triviality will be tantamount to undermining any genuine intention of improving rice production in the country.

This book will be inconclusive without mentioning post-harvest losses and storage in upland rice farming. There are various factors responsible for post-harvest losses in upland rice farming in the country, including biological, mechanical, and socio-economic factors. There is a need to study these factors to support farmers with their information management on the traditional practices and methods used to control post-harvest losses. It is not profitable for farmers to increase productivity if they incur huge post-harvest losses due to the lack of knowledge on loss control measures, poor handling and the unavailability of proper and adequate storage facilities.

In 1988, I conducted an agricultural extension 'method demonstration' on post-harvest losses as part of an Agriculture Field Day by the SLC/CCD project under the Council of Churches in Sierra Leone (CCSL), held in a village called Kpaku in the Pujehun District. The method demonstration took place on a rice farm that was specially prepared, during the season, for the agricultural show. The demonstration involved the traditional methods and measures that the farmers use to control and manage post-harvest-losses at each stage of the process starting from harvesting to milling.

Using two adjacently running lines of production with the matching sequence of farming activities ranging from harvesting, transporting to the farm hut, storage, threshing, parboiling, drying, milling and winnowing, one line was used to demonstrate the traditional methods and measures used by the farmers to control losses for each activity. The other line, running alongside, had similar activities in the corresponding order but without the loss control measures. This line served as the control for the comparisons. At the end of each line was the respective milled rice to serve as the 'result demonstration'.

The exercise aimed to highlight the diminishing returns from incurring post-harvest losses by increasing productivity without applying the necessary loss control measures. It was an awareness-building exercise for the farmers, professionals, and extension workers on the importance of managing post-harvest losses in upland rice farming.

For the observers from the CCSL and the representatives of the donor agencies from The World Council of Churches, Bread For The World, and Christian Aid, it was an eye-opener on how farmers manage post-harvest losses at the farmstead using their indigenous knowledge, methods and techniques.

Managing post-harvest losses should be part and parcel of the conversation on managing information on indigenous knowledge for increasing farmers' productivity in upland rice farming in Sierra Leone. Information management on traditional upland rice farming should be holistic and all-encompassing.

The final thrust of this book lies in the recommendation for the production of the translated versions, at the very least in parts, into the equivalent local languages in which the 'basic data' and 'data messages' on traditional upland rice farming have been translated. I envision the necessary translations will provide educational materials for teaching and learning about upland rice farming in Sierra Leone in the local languages.

Bibliography

Adikant Pradhan, S.K. Patil, T. Chandrakar, S.K. Nag and S.C. Mukherjee, 2019, Participatory Agricultural Resource Mapping for Crop Planning and Enhancing Productivity of Rural Areas, Bastar Plateau, Chhattisgarh, India. International Journal of Current Microbiology and Applied Sciences. ISSN: 2319-7706 Volume 8 Number 01 (2019)

Alavi M and Leidner D.E., 1997, Knowledge management system: emerging views and practice from the field. Fountainebleau: INSEAD (Tech. Rep. No. 97/97/TM).

Arokoyo T.,2003. ICTs for agriculture extension transformation. Proceeding of ICTs – transforming agriculture extension? CTA's observatory on ICT's Atherton

, J. H, 1979 'Early economies of Sierra Leone and Liberia: archaeological and historical reflections', in Dorhahn, V. and Isaac, B.

(eds.), 27-43 Google Scholar

Bateson, G.,1979. Mind and Nature: A Necessary Unity. New York: Bantam Books.

Bell, Martin (1979) "The Exploitation of Indigenous Knowledge or the Indigenous exploitation of Knowledge: Whose Use of What for What?" IDS Bulletin 10, no.2 (1979): 44-50.

Biggelaar, Christoffel den (1991) "Farming systems development: Synthesizing indigenous and scientific knowledge systems." Agriculture and Human Values volume 8, pages 25–36

Borneman E, 2014, Use of GIS in Agriculture, GIS Industry

Boserup, E. 1965. The Conditions of Agricultural Growth. London: Allen & Unwin; Chicago: Aldine Publishing Company, 1966.

Botanic Gardens Conservation International. 2018. "Plants for the Planet." Retrieved from http://www.bgci.org/about-us/index Brokensha, D. et al., 1980, Indigenous knowledge systems and Development.

Washington D C, University Press of America.

Bucking Shum S., 1998, "Negotiating the construction of organisational memories." In Information technology for knowledge management. Edited by U.M. Borghoff and R. Pareschi, pp. 55–78, Brlin: Spinger (Reprinted from: Journal of Universal Computer Science, 3(8), 1997, 899–928)

Buren E D., 2000. Cultural Aspects of Communication for Development. Translator: Falsafi, S. Tehran. IRIB Press. Iran, pp. 110-114. https://www.scirp.org/(S(351jmbntvnsjt1aadkozje))/reference/references papers.aspx?referenceid=1956031

Campbell, J.B. and Wynne, R.H., 2011, Introduction to Remote Sensing Fifth Edition. The Guilford Press, New York

Chambers R., 1983, Rural development, Putting the Last First, Co published in the United States with John Wiley & Sons, inc., New York

Chambers R., 1983, Farmers First, Intermediate Technology Publications, 103-105, Southampton Row, London WC!B 4HH, UK. Collins H.M., 2001, "Tacit knowledge, Trust and the Q of Sapphire". Social Studies of Science, p. 71–85 31(1) 2001.

Conklin E. J., 1996, Designing organisational memory; preserving intellectual property in a knowledge economy. Glebe Creek, MD: Cog Nexus Institute.

Corbin Tim, 2015, Agroforestry: Degraded Forest, The Food and Agricultural Organisation)

Davenport T and Prusak L, 1998, Working knowledge. How organisations manage what they know. Cambridge M.M.: Harvard Business School Press.

Dickenson J.P. et al., A Geography of the Third World, 1983, Published by Methuen & Co. Ltd. 11 New Fetter Lane, London EC4P 4EE

Dodd, J., and C. Jones. 2010. "Redefining the Role of Botanic Gardens—Towards a New Social Purpose. Research Centre for Museums and Galleries." Leicester.

Dornich K, Hammonds T, 2017, Use of GIS in Agriculture, Cornel College of Agriculture and Life Sciences, Cornel Small Farms Programme: http://www.cavalieragrow.ca/ifarm

Ekoja I (2003). Farmer's access to agricultural information in Nigeria. Bull. Am. Soc. Info. Sci. Technol., 29(6): 21–23.

Engel, P.G.H., & Seegers, S. (1989). Draft guidelines for the analysis of agricultural knowledge systems (AKSA). Unpublished Report. Agricultural University, Department of Extension Science, Wageningen, The Netherlands.

Estes, J. A., J. Terborgh, J. S. Brashares, M. E. Power, J. Berger, W.J. Bond, S.R. Carpenter, T.E. Essington, R.D. Holt, J.B.C. Jackson, R.J. Marquis, L. Oksanen, T. Oksanen, R.T. Paine, E.K. Pikitch, W.J. Ripple, S.A. Sandin, M. Scheffer, T.W. Schoener, J.B. Shurin, A.R.E. Sinclair, M.E. Soule, R. Virtanen, and D. A. Wardle., 2011. "Trophic Downgrading of Planet Earth." Science 333: 301–306. doi:10.1126/science.1205106.

FAO. 2013. "Fast Facts: The State of the World's Land and Water Resources (SOLAW)—Managing Systems at Risk." London and Rome.

FAO (2001). Knowledge and information for food security in Africa from traditional media to the Internet. Communication for Development Group, Sustainable Development Department. Rome: FAO.

Folke, C., S. Carpenter, B. Walker, M. Scheffer, T. Elmqvist, L. Gunderson, and S. C. Holling. 2004. "Regime Shifts, Resilience, and Biodiversity in Ecosystem Management." Annual Review of Ecology, Evolution, and Systematics 35 (1): 557–581. doi:10. 1146/annurev.ecolsys.35.021103.105711

Garforth C, 1993, lecture notes, Agriculture Extension and Rural Development, Department of Agricultural Extension and Rural Development at the University of Reading, UK Gareth E. Jones, Maurice John Rolls, R. B.

Tranter, Published 1987 by University of Reading, Agriculture Extension and Rural Development Centre

Gifford, R., 2011. "The Dragons of Inaction: Psychological Barriers That Limit Climate Change Mitigation and Adaptation." The American Psychologist 66 (4): 290–302. doi:10.1037/a0023566

Glanville, R. R. (1933), Sierra Leone: rice cultivation. Report on a visit to Ceylon and South India with proposal for Sierra Leone, Freetown: Government Printer.

Glanville, R. R. (1938), 'Rice Production on Swamps', Sierra Leone Agricultural Notes, 7

Glazer R., 1998, "Measuring the knower: towards a theory of knowledge equity", California Management Review, 40(3), 175–194. Global Agriculture Maps – Farming Visualized/Available at URL: https://gisgeography.com/agriculture-maps-global-farming/ –Title from Screen. –Date of Access: 11 November 2019.

Goguen J. A., 1997, "Toward a social, ethical theory of information in Social science technical systems and cooperative work; beyond the great ivied", edited by G.C. Bowker, Susan L, Star W., Turner and L. Gasser, pp. 27–56.

Mahwah, NJ; Lawrence Erlbaum Associates.

Hildreth P, Wright P and Kimble C., 1999, "Knowledge management; are we missing something?" in; 4th UKAIS Conference, York, UK, pp 347–356.
London McGraw Hill.

Hildreth P and Kimble C., 2002, "The duality of knowledge". Information Research, Vol. 8, No. 1, October 2002.

Huang K., 1997, "Capitalising collective knowledge for wining executives teamwork", Journal of Knowledge management 1(2) 149–156. Jean M. Due and Gerald L. Karr, 1973, Strategies for increasing rice production in Sierra Leone, African studies review : the journal of the African Studies Association. East Lansing, Mich. [u.a.] : Cambridge Univ.
Press, ISSN 0002-0206, ZDB-ID 410083-9. Vol. 16.1973, 1, p. 23-71

Jordan (1954), Development of Rice Research in Sierra Leone, Tropical Agriculture Vol. XXXY

Juma, C, 1987, Ecological Complexity and agricultural innovation: the use of indigenous resources in Bungama, Kenya. IDS Workshop

Kimble C. Hildreth P and Wright P., 2001, "Community of practice: going virtual", in Knowledge management and business innovation, edited by Y. Malhotra, pp. 216–230, Hershey, PA: Idea Group. Retrieved 26th September 2002.

Kogut B., and Zander V., 1992, "Knowledge of the firm, Combinative capabilities and the replication of technology", Organisation Science, 3(3)
383–397. Kyem P.A.K, Saku J. C, 2017, Web-Based GIS and the Future of Participatory
GIS Applications within Local and Indigenous Communities, (First published, December 2017)

Lamptey R B, Sambo I A, Hassan A., 2017, "Disseminating and Promoting Agriculture Information through Library and Information Services in Ghana". Qualitative and Quantitative Methods in Libraries, [S.l.], v. 5, n. 4, p. 901-907, Apr. 2017. ISSN 2241-1925.

Leonard D and Sensiper S., 1998, "The role of tacit knowledge in group innovation", California Management Review, 40(3), pp.112–132.

Little, K. (1951), The Mende rice farm and its cost. Zaire 5 (3): 227–273

Louise O. Fresco Herman G.J, Huizing Hermen Van Keulen Henk A. Luning Robert, Schipper A., 1999, Land Evaluation and Farming Systems Analysis For Land Use Planning FAO working document Third edition 1992

Lubchenco, J., 1998. "Entering the Century of the Environment: A New Social Contract for Science." Science 279 (5350): 491–497. doi:10.1126/science.279.5350.491

Luft Joseph and Ingham Harry, 1955, "The Johari Window"

Martha Johnson, 2014, Capturing Traditional Environmental Knowledge.

Research on Traditional Environmental Knowledge: Its Development and Its Role By, Dene Cultural Institute, Yellowknife, NWT, Canada. What is Traditional.

Mahoney D, 2016, Anthropology of Africa (Reviewed April 2021).

Mbiti J S, African Religions and Philosophy: Published by Heinemann; 2nd Revised & Enlarged edition (28 Feb. 1990, 2nd edition)

McCarthy S. Africa: The challenge of Transformation, 1994, I. B. Tauris & Co. Publishers, London. New York.

Melissa K. Nelson, Daniel Shilling, 2018, Traditional Ecological Knowledge Learning from Indigenous Practices for Environmental Sustainability October Cambridge University Press

Mohammad Reza Nazari and Md Salleh Bin Hj Hassan, 2011, Salleh Md "The role of television in the enhancement of farmers' agricultural knowledge." African Journal of Agricultural Research Vol. 6(4), pp. 931-936, 18 February, 2011.

Moore Sally Falk, 1994, Anthropology and Africa: Changing Perspectives on a changing scene, Charlottesville, University Press Virginia.

Nazari MR, Hasbullah AH, Parhizkar S, Shirazi A, Marioriad R., 2009. The impact of visuals: Using Television programmes to transform environmental health concepts to people. J. Appl. Sci., (JAS), 8(2): 2619-2624.

Nonaka I., 1991, "The knowledge Creating company", Harvard Business Review, 69 (Nov.–Dec.), pp. 96–104. Offsey S., 1997, "knowledge management: Linking people to knowledge for bottom line results," Journal of Knowledge management, 1(2), 113–112.

Philip Stanhope, 4th Earl of Chesterfield ed. 1827: "Letters Written by the Earl of Chesterfield to His Son"

Polani M., 1967, The tacit dimension, London: Routledge and Kegan Paul.

Raimo Nikkilä, Ilkka Seilonen, Kari Koskinen, 2010, Computers and Electronics in Agriculture. Software architecture for farm management information systems in precision agriculture Volume 70,Issue 2, pages 328 – 336.

Raskin, P., T. Banuri, G. Gallopin, P. Gutman, A. Hammond, K. Robert, and R. Swart. 2002. The Great Transition: The Promise and Lure of the Times Ahead. Boston: Stockholm Environment Institute Rees, W. E., 2002. "Globalization and Sustainability: Conflict or Convergence?" Bulletin of Science, Technology & Society, 22 (4): 249–268. doi:10.1177/0270467602022004001

Rulke D., Zaheer S. and Anderson M., 1998, "Transactive Knowledge and performance in the retail food industry". Paper delivered at the Stern School of Business conference on management and Organisational cognition, New York City. New York, NY: New York University, Leonard Stern School of business.

Richards P., 1979, 'Community Environmental Knowledge in Africa Rural Development', IDS Bulletin p 28 – 35

Richards P., 1985, Indigenous Agricultural Revolution, Hutchinson, London and Westview Press, Boulder, Colorado

Rondeau Emmanuel, 2015, Agroforestry: Healthy forest, The Food and Agricultural Organisation)

Sathaye, J., A. Najam, C. Cocklin, T. Heller, F. Lecocq, J. Llanes-Regueiro, J. Pan, et al., 2007. "Sustainable Development and Mitigation." In Climate Change 2007: Mitigation, edited by B. Metz, O. R. Davidson, P. R. Bosch, R. Dave, and L. A. Meyer (Contributi, p. 54). Cambridge, UK: Cambridge University Press. doi: 10.105 //palgrave.jba.2950072

Saville P. S. & J.E.D. Fox (1967), Trees of Sierra Leone (based on fieldwork 1062-1966)

Seely Brown J and Duguid P., 1998, "Organising Knowledge", California Management Review, 40(3), p. 90–111.

Suzuki, D., and A. McConnell. 2007. The Sacred Balance: Rediscovering Our Place in Nature. Vancouver: Greystone Books.

Swam J., Newell S., Scarborough H. and Hislop D., 1999, "Knowledge management and innovation; Network and networking", Journal of Knowledge Management 3(4) pp. 262–275.

Teece D. J., 1998, "Research directions for knowledge management", California management Review, 40 (3), 89–292.

Tricker R I 1988 Information resource management—a cross-cultural perspective—Information & Management. Volume 15, Issue 1, 1988, Pages 37-46

Tripathi N, Shefali and Bhattarya, 2017, Integrating Indigenous Knowledge and GIS for Participatory Natural Resource Management: State-of-the-Practice. (First published, December 2017).

Trung N.H., Tri L.Q., Van Mensvoort M.E.F. and Bregt A.K., 2006, Application of GIS in Land-Use Planning, A Case Study in The Coastal Mekong Delta of Vietnam. International Symposium on Geoinformatics for Spatial Infrastructure Development in Earth and Allied Sciences Van den Ban A. W. and Hawkins H. S., 1988, Agricultural Extension,

Longman Scientific Technical, Co published in the United States with John Wiley & Sons, inc., New York

Walker, B., S. C. Holling, R. S. Carpenter, and A. Kinzig. 2004. "Resilience, Adaptability and Transformability in Social–Ecological Systems." Ecology and society 9 (2). Article id. 5 Weber, E. U., and J.E. Johnson. 2012. "Psychology and behavioural economics lessons for the design of a green growth strategy (No. WPS 6240)."

Washington, DC: Whitmarsh, L., I. Lorenzoni, and S. O'Neill. 2012. Engaging the Public with Climate Change: Behaviour Change and Communication. London: Routledge.

Wikipedia (2007), Tacit Knowledge; Properties of tacit knowledge.

Williams, S. J., J. P. G. Jones, M. J. Gibbons, and C. Clubbe. 2015. "Botanic Gardens can Positively Influence Visitors' Environmental Attitudes." Biodiversity and Conservation 24 (7): 1609–1620. doi:10.1007/s10531-015-0879-7

Will Kenton, 2020, "Seasonality". Reviewed by Robert C. Kelly.

Yan-e D., 2011, "Design of Intelligent Agriculture Management Information System Based on IoT," Fourth International Conference on Intelligent Computation Technology and Automation, 2011, pp. 1045-1049, doi: 10.1109/ICICTA.2011.262.

Zalasiewicz, J., M. Williams, W. Steffen, and P. Crutzen. 2010. "The new world of the Anthropocene." Environmental Science and Technology 44 (7): 2228–2231

Book Reviews

I find this book not only very interesting to read, the author immensely succeeded in achieving its intended purpose, vis-á-vis preserving indigenous knowledge in upland rice farming in Sierra Leone. The book equally serves as an excellent piece of research work. With developments in computer science and information management, the timing of this book could not have been more precise. It is a given that some indigenous knowledge may have been lost over the past decades however, it is never too late to preserve what is still out there for the benefit of humanity!

Mr Eya David Macauley

In all intent and purposes, this study is premised on case studies in the Pujehun District in Sierra Leone. Jim's timely intervention and contribution to the ongoing crucial and nagging Africa's Indigenous Knowledge Systems (IKS) debate shares time-tested, prudent and empirical significance of indigenous knowledge. Essentially the author presents the world with dated realities of how "integrating informal and formal farming knowledge enhance sustainable and resilient agriculture". Hopefully, African indigenous farmers, including such stakeholders as researchers and authors, will receive recognition as partners and co-instigators of sundry formal and informal knowledge generation, as well as be brought together as catalysts of innovative ways for food sustenance around the world, particularly on the African continent.

Dr O.C. Akinola,

"A potent way of expanding the horizon of knowledge and empowering mankind is to share experiences."

This book, entitled 'Indigenous knowledge on traditional upland rice farming in Sierra Leone and how it can be used in information management', is undoubtedly an excellent means of sharing information and expanding people's knowledge of farming practices by local communities with long histories of engagement with their natural environments. Mr Jim Patewa, therefore, deserves to be commended for the painstaking exercise in piecing together extracts from the multiple case studies that informed this book. Whilst a case study methodology is time-consuming given the level of analysis required, it resulted in the production of rich information and an in-depth understanding of indigenous knowledge on traditional upland rice farming in the Pujehun District in Sierra Leone. Such an understanding may have practical utility among farming communities, including traditional upland farmers in other districts of Sierra Leone.

This is a well-written book with a logical and coherent structure with seven distinct but interrelated chapters with comprehensive accounts of indigenous knowledge farming practices, which are gradually disappearing. This book, therefore, contributes to keeping the subject of indigenous knowledge of farming practices alive. It also provides opportunities for Sierra Leoneans and non-Sierra Leoneans with an interest in agriculture to gain insight into the historical context of this subject, maintain its significance and promote sustainable and resilient agriculture. Hence, every Sierra Leonean, who strives to promote sustainable and resilient agriculture, particularly upland rice farming must set aside time to read this text and share their knowledge and understanding of the same.

Professor Peter Sandy.

Index